Airman Knowledge Testing Supplement for Commercial Pilot

2018

U.S. Department of Transportation
FEDERAL AVIATION ADMINISTRATION
Flight Standards Service

Preface

This testing supplement supersedes FAA-CT-8080-1D, Airman Knowledge Testing Supplement for Commercial Pilot, dated 2016.

This Airman Knowledge Testing Supplement is designed by the Federal Aviation Administration (FAA) Flight Standards Service. It is intended for use by Airman Knowledge Testing (AKT) Organization Designation Authorization (ODA) Holders and other entities approved and/or authorized to administer airman knowledge tests on behalf of the FAA in the following knowledge areas:

Commercial Pilot—Airplane (CAX)
Commercial Pilot—Glider (CGX)
Commercial Pilot—Lighter-Than-Air–Airship (CLA)
Commercial Pilot—Rotorcraft/Gyroplane (CRG)
Commercial Pilot—Rotorcraft/Helicopter (CRH)
Commercial Pilot—Balloon Gas (CBG)
Commercial Pilot—Balloon–Hot Air (CBH)
Military Competence for Commercial Pilot Certification, Non-Category Specific (MCN)

Comments regarding this supplement, or any Airman Testing publication, should be emailed to AFS630comments@faa.gov .

Contents

Appendix 1

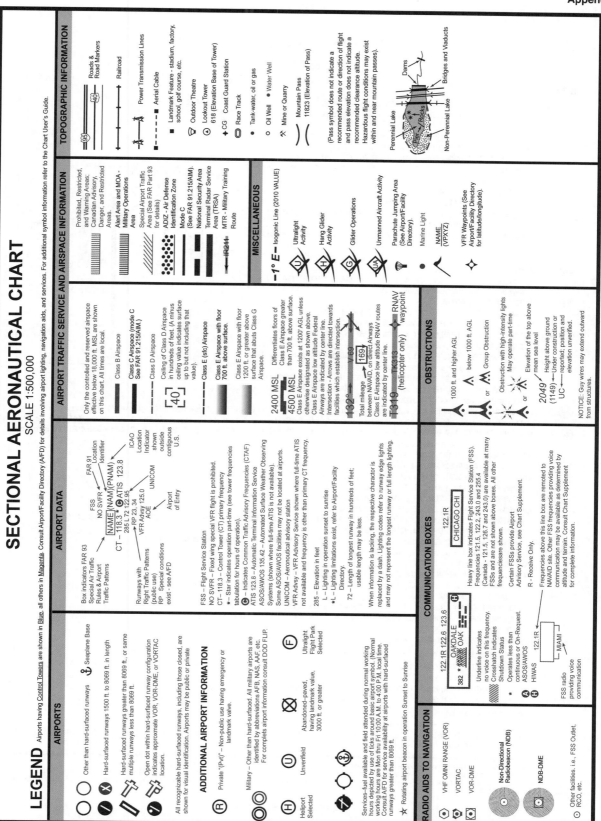

Legend 1. Sectional Aeronautical Chart.

12　　　AIRPORT/FACILITY DIRECTORY LEGEND

SAMPLE

① CITY NAME

② ③ ④ ⑤ ⑥ ⑦ ⑧

AIRPORT NAME (ALTERNATE NAME) (LTS)(KLTS) CIV/MIL 3 N UTC–6(–5DT) N34°41.93′ W99°20.20′ JACKSONVILLE COPTER

⑪ ⑫ ⑬ ⑭ ⑮ ⑯ ⑰ H–4G, L–19C

200 B TPA—1000(800) AOE LRA Class IV, ARFF Index A NOTAM FILE ORL Not insp. IAP, DIAP, AD

⑨

⑱ **RWY 18–36:** H12004X200 (ASPH–CONC–GRVD)

S–90, D–160, 2D–300 PCN 80 R/B/W/T HIRL CL

RWY 18: RLLS. MALSF. TDZL. REIL. PAPI(P2R)—GA 3.0° TCH 36′.

RVR–TMR. Thld dsplcd 300′. Trees. Rgt tfc. 0.3% up.

RWY 36: ALSF1. 0.4% down.

RWY 09–27: H6000X150 (ASPH) MIRL

RWY 173–353: H3515X150 (ASPH–PFC) AUW PCN 59 F/A/W/T

⑲ **LAND AND HOLD–SHORT OPERATIONS**

LDG RWY	HOLD–SHORT POINT	AVBL LDG DIST
RWY 18	09–27	6500
RWY 36	09–27	5400

⑳ **RUNWAY DECLARED DISTANCE INFORMATION**

RWY 18: TORA–12004 TODA–12004 ASDA–11704 LDA–11504

RWY 36: TORA–12004 TODA–12004 ASDA–12004 LDA–11704

㉑ **ARRESTING GEAR/SYSTEM**

RWY 18 HOOK E5 (65′ OVRN) BAK–14 BAK–12B (1650′)

BAK–14 BAK–12B (1087′) HOOK E5 (74′ OVRN) **RWY 36**

㉒ **SERVICE:** S4 **FUEL** 100LL, JET A **OX** 1, 3 **LGT** ACTIVATE MALSR Rwy 29, REIL Rwy 11, VASI Rwy 11, HIRL Rwy 11–29, PAPI Rwy 17 and Rwy 35, MIRL Rwy 17–35—CTAF. **MILITARY**— **A–GEAR** E–5 connected on dep end, disconnected on apch end.

JASU 3(AM32A–60) 2(A/M32A–86) **FUEL** J8(Mil)(NC–100, A)

FLUID W SP PRESAIR LOX **OIL** O–128 **MAINT** S1 Mon–Fri 1000–2200Z‡

TRAN ALERT Avbl 1300–0200Z‡ svc limited weekends.

㉓ **AIRPORT REMARKS:** Special Air Traffic Rules—Part 93, see Regulatory Notices. Attended 1200–0300Z‡. Parachute Jumping. Deer invof arpt. Heavy jumbo jet training surface to 9000′. Twy A clsd indef. Flight Notification Service (ADCUS) avbl.

㉔ **MILITARY REMARKS:** ANG PPR/Official Business Only. Base OPS DSN 638–4390, C503–335–4222. Ctc Base OPS 15 minutes prior to ldg and after dep. Limited tran parking.

㉕ **AIRPORT MANAGER:** (580) 481–5739

㉖ **WEATHER DATA SOURCES:** AWOS–1 120.3 (202) 426–8000. LAWRS.

㉗ **COMMUNICATIONS:** SFA **CTAF** 122.8 **UNICOM** 122.95 **ATIS** 127.25 273.5 (202) 426–8003 **PTD** 372.2

NAME FSS (ORL) on arpt. 123.65 122.65 122.2

NAME RCO 112.2T 112.1R (NAME RADIO)

Ⓡ **NAME APP/DEP CON** 128.35 257.725 (1200–0400Z‡)

TOWER 119.65 255.6 (1200–0400Z‡) **GND CON** 121.7 **GCO** 135.075 (ORLANDO CLNC) **CLNC DEL** 125.55

CPDLC D–HZWXR, D–TAXI, DCL (LOGON KMEM)

NAME COMD POST (GERONIMO) 311.0 321.4 6761 **PMSV METRO** 239.8 **NAME OPS** 257.5

㉘ **AIRSPACE:** CLASS B See VFR Terminal Area Chart.

㉙ **VOR TEST FACILITY (VOT):** 116.7

㉚ **RADIO AIDS TO NAVIGATION:** NOTAM FILE ORL. VHF/DF ctc FSS.

(H) VORTAC 112.2 MCO Chan 59 N28°32.55′ W81°20.12′ at fld. 1110/8E.

(H) TACAN Chan 29 CBU (109.2) N28°32.65′ W81°21.12′ at fld. 1115/8E.

HERNY NDB (LOM) 221 OR N28°37.40′ W81°21.05′ 177° 5.4 NM to fld.

ILS/DME 108.5 I–ORL Chan 22 Rwy 18. Class IIE. LOM HERNY NDB.

ASR/PAR (1200–0400Z‡)

㉛ **COMM/NAV/WEATHER REMARKS:** Emerg frequency 121.5 not avbl at twr.

• • • • • • • • • • • • • • • • • •

HELIPAD H1: H100X75 (ASPH)

HELIPAD H2: H60X60 (ASPH)

HELIPORT REMARKS: Helipad H1 lctd on general aviation side and H2 lctd on air carrier side of arpt.

① • • • • • • • • • • • • • • • •

187 TPA 1000(813)

WATERWAY 15–33: 5000X425 (WATER)

SEAPLANE REMARKS: Birds roosting and feeding areas along river banks. Seaplanes operating adjacent to SW side of arpt not visible from twr and are required to ctc twr.

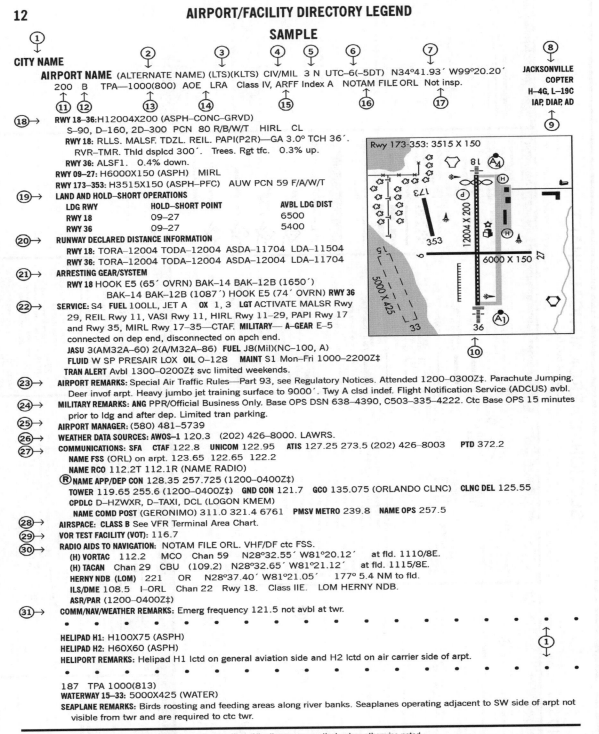

Rwy 173-353: 3515 X 150

All bearings and radials are magnetic unless otherwise specified. All mileages are nautical unless otherwise noted.
All times are Coordinated Universal Time (UTC) except as noted. All elevations are in feet above/below Mean Sea Level (MSL) unless otherwise noted.
The horizontal reference datum of this publication is North American Datum of 1983 (NAD83), which for charting purposes is considered equivalent to World Geodetic System 1984 (WGS 84).

SC, 1 FEB 20XX to 29 MAR 20XX

Legend 2. Chart Supplement.

SKETCH LEGEND

18032

RUNWAYS/LANDING AREAS

Hard Surfaced . . . .

Metal Surface . . . .

Sod, Gravel, etc. . . . .

Light Plane, ...
Ski Landing Area or Water

Under Construction . . . . .

Closed Rwy . . . .

Closed Pavement . . . .

Helicopter Landings Area . . . . (H)

Displaced Threshold . . . .

Taxiway, Apron and Stopways . .

MISCELLANEOUS BASE AND CULTURAL FEATURES

Buildings . . . .

Power Lines . . . . —T——T—

Fence . . . .

Towers . . . .

Wind Turbine. . . . .

Tanks . . . .

Oil Well . . . .

Smoke Stack . . . .

Obstruction 5812

Controlling Obstruction . . . . +5812

Trees . . . .

Populated Places . . . .

Cuts and Fills . . . . . . Cut / Fill

Cliffs and Depressions . .

Ditch . . . .

Hill . . . .

RADIO AIDS TO NAVIGATION

VORTAC . . . ⬡   VOR . . . . ⬡

VOR/DME . . ▢   NDB . . . .

TACAN . . . . ⬠   NDB/DME . . . .

DME . . . . ▢

MISCELLANEOUS AERONAUTICAL FEATURES

Airport Beacon . . . . ☆ ✪

Wind Cone . . . .

Landing Tee . . . .

Tetrahedron . . . .

Control Tower . . . . 🏢 or **TWR**

When control tower and rotating beacon are co-located beacon symbol will be used and further identified as TWR.

APPROACH LIGHTING SYSTEMS

A dot "•" portrayed with approach lighting letter identifier indicates sequenced flashing lights (F) installed with the approach lighting system e.g. Ⓐ₁ Negative symbology, e.g., Ⓐ₁ Ⓥ indicates Pilot Controlled Lighting (PCL).

Runway Centerline Lighting . . . . .

Ⓐ Approach Lighting System ALSF-2 . .

Ⓐ₁ Approach Lighting System ALSF-1 . .

Ⓐ₂ Short Approach Lighting System SALS/SALSF . . . .

Ⓐ₃ Simplified Short Approach Lighting System (SSALR) with RAIL . . . . .

Ⓐ₄ Medium Intensity Approach Lighting System (MALS and MALSF)/(SSALS and SSALF) . . . .

Ⓐ₅ Medium Intensity Approach Lighting System (MALSR) and RAIL . . . . . .

Ⓧ Omnidirectional Approach Lighting System (ODALS) . . . .

Ⓓ Navy Parallel Row and Cross Bar . . .

Ⓣ Air Force Overrun . . . .

Ⓥ Visual Approach Slope Indicator with Standard Threshold Clearance provided

Ⓥ₂ Pulsating Visual Approach Slope Indicator (PVASI)

Ⓥ₃ Visual Approach Slope Indicator with a threshold crossing height to accomodate long bodied or jumbo aircraft

Ⓥ₄ Tri-color Visual Approach Slope Indicator (TRCV)

Ⓥ₅ Approach Path Alignment Panel (APAP)

Ⓟ Precision Approach Path Indicator (PAPI)

SC, 1 FEB 20XX to 29 MAR 20XX

Legend 3. Chart Supplement.

14   AIRPORT/FACILITY DIRECTORY LEGEND

LEGEND

This directory is a listing of data on record with the FAA on public–use airports, military airports and selected private–use airports specifically requested by the Department of Defense (DoD) for which a DoD Instrument Approach Procedure has been published in the U.S. Terminal Procedures Publication. Additionally this listing contains data for associated terminal control facilities, air route traffic control centers, and radio aids to navigation within the conterminous United States, Puerto Rico and the Virgin Islands. Civil airports and joint Civil/Military airports which are open to the public are listed alphabetically by state, associated city and airport name and cross–referenced by airport name. Military airports and private–use (limited civil access) joint Military/Civil airports are listed alphabetically by state and official airport name and cross–referenced by associated city name. Navaids, flight service stations and remote communication outlets that are associated with an airport, but with a different name, are listed alphabetically under their own name, as well as under the airport with which they are associated.

The listing of an airport as open to the public in this directory merely indicates the airport operator's willingness to accommodate transient aircraft, and does not represent that the airport conforms with any Federal or local standards, or that it has been approved for use on the part of the general public. Military airports, private–use airports, and private–use (limited civil access) joint Military/Civil airports are open to civil pilots only in an emergency or with prior permission. See Special Notice Section, Civil Use of Military Fields.

The information on obstructions is taken from reports submitted to the FAA. Obstruction data has not been verified in all cases. Pilots are cautioned that objects not indicated in this tabulation (or on the airports sketches and/or charts) may exist which can create a hazard to flight operation. Detailed specifics concerning services and facilities tabulated within this directory are contained in the Aeronautical Information Manual, Basic Flight Information and ATC Procedures.

The legend items that follow explain in detail the contents of this Directory and are keyed to the circled numbers on the sample on the preceding pages.

① CITY/AIRPORT NAME

Civil and joint Civil/Military airports which are open to the public are listed alphabetically by state and associated city. Where the city name is different from the airport name the city name will appear on the line above the airport name. Airports with the same associated city name will be listed alphabetically by airport name and will be separated by a dashed rule line. A solid rule line will separate all others. FAA approved helipads and seaplane landing areas associated with a land airport will be separated by a dotted line. Military airports and private–use (limited civil access) joint Military/Civil airports are listed alphabetically by state and official airport name.

② ALTERNATE NAME

Alternate names, if any, will be shown in parentheses.

③ LOCATION IDENTIFIER

The location identifier is a three or four character FAA code followed by a four–character ICAO code, when assigned, to airports. If two different military codes are assigned, both codes will be shown with the primary operating agency's code listed first. These identifiers are used by ATC in lieu of the airport name in flight plans, flight strips and other written records and computer operations. Zeros will appear with a slash to differentiate them from the letter "O".

④ OPERATING AGENCY

Airports within this directory are classified into two categories, Military/Federal Government and Civil airports open to the general public, plus selected private–use airports. The operating agency is shown for military, private–use and joint use airports. The operating agency is shown by an abbreviation as listed below. When an organization is a tenant, the abbreviation is enclosed in parenthesis. No classification indicates the airport is open to the general public with no military tenant.

A	US Army	MC	Marine Corps
AFRC	Air Force Reserve Command	MIL/CIV	Joint Use Military/Civil Limited Civil Access
AF	US Air Force	N	Navy
ANG	Air National Guard	NAF	Naval Air Facility
AR	US Army Reserve	NAS	Naval Air Station
ARNG	US Army National Guard	NASA	National Air and Space Administration
CG	US Coast Guard	P	US Civil Airport Wherein Permit Covers Use by Transient Military Aircraft
CIV/MIL	Joint Use Civil/Military Open to the Public		
DND	Department of National Defense Canada	PVT	Private Use Only (Closed to the Public)

⑤ AIRPORT LOCATION

Airport location is expressed as distance and direction from the center of the associated city in nautical miles and cardinal points, e.g., 4 NE.

⑥ TIME CONVERSION

Hours of operation of all facilities are expressed in Coordinated Universal Time (UTC) and shown as "Z" time. The directory indicates the number of hours to be subtracted from UTC to obtain local standard time and local daylight saving time UTC–5(–4DT). The symbol ‡ indicates that during periods of Daylight Saving Time (DST) effective hours will be one hour earlier than shown. In those areas where daylight saving time is not observed the (–4DT) and ‡ will not be shown. Daylight saving time is in effect from 0200 local time the second Sunday in March to 0200 local time the first Sunday in November. Canada and all U.S. Conterminous States observe daylight saving time except Arizona and Puerto Rico, and the Virgin Islands. If the state observes daylight saving time and the operating times are other than daylight saving times, the operating hours will include the dates, times and no ‡ symbol will be shown, i.e., April 15–Aug 31 0630–1700Z, Sep 1–Apr 14 0600–1700Z.

Legend 4. Chart Supplement.

AIRPORT/FACILITY DIRECTORY LEGEND

⑦ **GEOGRAPHIC POSITION OF AIRPORT—AIRPORT REFERENCE POINT (ARP)**

Positions are shown as hemisphere, degrees, minutes and hundredths of a minute and represent the approximate geometric center of all usable runway surfaces.

⑧ **CHARTS**

Charts refer to the Sectional Chart and Low and High Altitude Enroute Chart and panel on which the airport or facility is depicted. Helicopter Chart depictions will be indicated as COPTER. IFR Gulf of Mexico West and IFR Gulf of Mexico Central will be referenced as GOMW and GOMC.

⑨ **INSTRUMENT APPROACH PROCEDURES, AIRPORT DIAGRAMS**

IAP indicates an airport for which a prescribed (Public Use) FAA Instrument Approach Procedure has been published. DIAP indicates an airport for which a prescribed DoD Instrument Approach Procedure has been published in the U.S. Terminal Procedures. See the Special Notice Section of this directory, Civil Use of Military Fields and the Aeronautical Information Manual 5–4–5 Instrument Approach Procedure Charts for additional information. AD indicates an airport for which an airport diagram has been published. Airport diagrams are located in the back of each Chart Supplement volume alphabetically by associated city and airport name.

⑩ **AIRPORT SKETCH**

The airport sketch, when provided, depicts the airport and related topographical information as seen from the air and should be used in conjunction with the text. It is intended as a guide for pilots in VFR conditions. Symbology that is not self–explanatory will be reflected in the sketch legend. The airport sketch will be oriented with True North at the top. Airport sketches will be added incrementally.

⑪ **ELEVATION**

The highest point of an airport's usable runways measured in feet from mean sea level. When elevation is sea level it will be indicated as "00". When elevation is below sea level a minus "–" sign will precede the figure.

⑫ **ROTATING LIGHT BEACON**

B indicates rotating beacon is available. Rotating beacons operate sunset to sunrise unless otherwise indicated in the AIRPORT REMARKS or MILITARY REMARKS segment of the airport entry.

⑬ **TRAFFIC PATTERN ALTITUDE**

Traffic Pattern Altitude (TPA)—The first figure shown is TPA above mean sea level. The second figure in parentheses is TPA above airport elevation. Multiple TPA shall be shown as "TPA—See Remarks" and detailed information shall be shown in the Airport or Military Remarks Section. Traffic pattern data for USAF bases, USN facilities, and U.S. Army airports (including those on which ACC or U.S. Army is a tenant) that deviate from standard pattern altitudes shall be shown in Military Remarks.

⑭ **AIRPORT OF ENTRY, LANDING RIGHTS, AND CUSTOMS USER FEE AIRPORTS**

U.S. CUSTOMS USER FEE AIRPORT—Private Aircraft operators are frequently required to pay the costs associated with customs processing.

AOE—Airport of Entry. A customs Airport of Entry where permission from U.S. Customs is not required to land. However, at least one hour advance notice of arrival is required.

LRA—Landing Rights Airport. Application for permission to land must be submitted in advance to U.S. Customs. At least one hour advance notice of arrival is required.

NOTE: Advance notice of arrival at both an AOE and LRA airport may be included in the flight plan when filed in Canada or Mexico. Where Flight Notification Service (ADCUS) is available the airport remark will indicate this service. This notice will also be treated as an application for permission to land in the case of an LRA. Although advance notice of arrival may be relayed to Customs through Mexico, Canada, and U.S. Communications facilities by flight plan, the aircraft operator is solely responsible for ensuring that Customs receives the notification. (See Customs, Immigration and Naturalization, Public Health and Agriculture Department requirements in the International Flight Information Manual for further details.)

U.S. CUSTOMS AIR AND SEA PORTS, INSPECTORS AND AGENTS

Northeast Sector (New England and Atlantic States—ME to MD)	407–975–1740
Southeast Sector (Atlantic States—DC, WV, VA to FL)	407–975–1780
Central Sector (Interior of the US, including Gulf states—MS, AL, LA)	407–975–1760
Southwest East Sector (OK and eastern TX)	407–975–1840
Southwest West Sector (Western TX, NM and AZ)	407–975–1820
Pacific Sector (WA, OR, CA, HI and AK)	407–975–1800

⑮ **CERTIFICATED AIRPORT (14 CFR PART 139)**

Airports serving Department of Transportation certified carriers and certified under 14 CFR part 139 are indicated by the Class and the ARFF Index; e.g. Class I, ARFF Index A, which relates to the availability of crash, fire, rescue equipment. Class I airports can have an ARFF Index A through E, depending on the aircraft length and scheduled departures. Class II, III, and IV will always carry an Index A.

AIRPORT CLASSIFICATIONS

Type of Air Carrier Operation	Class I	Class II	Class III	Class IV
Scheduled Air Carrier Aircraft with 31 or more passenger seats	X			
Unscheduled Air Carrier Aircraft with 31 or more passengers seats	X	X		X
Scheduled Air Carrier Aircraft with 10 to 30 passenger seats	X	X	X	

SC, 1 FEB 20XX to 29 MAR 20XX

Legend 5. Chart Supplement.

AIRPORT/FACILITY DIRECTORY LEGEND

16

INDICES AND AIRCRAFT RESCUE AND FIRE FIGHTING EQUIPMENT REQUIREMENTS

Airport Index	Required No. Vehicles	Aircraft Length	Scheduled Departures	Agent + Water for Foam
A	1	<90′	≥1	500#DC or HALON 1211 or 450#DC + 100 gal H_2O
B	1 or 2	≥90′, <126′	≥5	Index A + 1500 gal H_2O
		≥126′, <159′	<5	
C	2 or 3	≥126′, <159′	≥5	Index A + 3000 gal H_2O
		≥159′, <200′	<5	
D	3	≥159′, <200′	≥5	Index A + 4000 gal H_2O
		>200′	<5	
E	3	≥200′	≥5	Index A + 6000 gal H_2O

> Greater Than; < Less Than; ≥ Equal or Greater Than; ≤ Equal or Less Than; H_2O–Water; DC–Dry Chemical.

NOTE: The listing of ARFF index does not necessarily assure coverage for non–air carrier operations or at other than prescribed times for air carrier. ARFF Index Ltd.—indicates ARFF coverage may or may not be available, for information contact airport manager prior to flight.

⑯ NOTAM SERVICE

All public use landing areas are provided NOTAM service. A NOTAM FILE identifier is shown for individual landing areas, e.g., "NOTAM FILE BNA". See the AIM, Basic Flight Information and ATC Procedures for a detailed description of NOTAMs. Current NOTAMs are available from flight service stations at 1–800–WX–BRIEF (992–7433) or online through the FAA PilotWeb at https://pilotweb.nas.faa.gov. Military NOTAMs are available using the Defense Internet NOTAM Service (DINS) at https://www.notams.faa.gov. Pilots flying to or from airports not available through the FAA PilotWeb or DINS can obtain assistance from Flight Service.

⑰ FAA INSPECTION

All airports not inspected by FAA will be identified by the note: Not insp. This indicates that the airport information has been provided by the owner or operator of the field.

⑱ RUNWAY DATA

Runway information is shown on two lines. That information common to the entire runway is shown on the first line while information concerning the runway ends is shown on the second or following line. Runway direction, surface, length, width, weight bearing capacity, lighting, and slope, when available are shown for each runway. Multiple runways are shown with the longest runway first. Direction, length, width, and lighting are shown for sea–lanes. The full dimensions of helipads are shown, e.g., 50X150. Runway data that requires clarification will be placed in the remarks section.

RUNWAY DESIGNATION

Runways are normally numbered in relation to their magnetic orientation rounded off to the nearest 10 degrees. Parallel runways can be designated L (left)/R (right)/C (center). Runways may be designated as Ultralight or assault strips. Assault strips are shown by magnetic bearing.

RUNWAY DIMENSIONS

Runway length and width are shown in feet. Length shown is runway end to end including displaced thresholds, but excluding those areas designed as overruns.

RUNWAY SURFACE AND SURFACE TREATMENT

Runway lengths prefixed by the letter "H" indicate that the runways are hard surfaced (concrete, asphalt, or part asphalt–concrete). If the runway length is not prefixed, the surface is sod, clay, etc. The runway surface composition is indicated in parentheses after runway length as follows:

(AFSC)—Aggregate friction seal coat
(AM2)—Temporary metal planks coated with nonskid material
(ASPH)—Asphalt
(CONC)—Concrete
(DIRT)—Dirt
(GRVD)—Grooved

(GRVL)—Gravel, or cinders
(MATS)—Pierced steel planking, landing mats, membranes
(PEM)—Part concrete, part asphalt
(PFC)—Porous friction courses
(PSP)—Pierced steel plank
(RFSC)—Rubberized friction seal coat

(SAND)—Sand
(TURF)—Turf

(TRTD)—Treated
(WC)—Wire combed

SC, 1 FEB 20XX to 29 MAR 20XX

Legend 6. Chart Supplement.

AIRPORT/FACILITY DIRECTORY LEGEND

RUNWAY WEIGHT BEARING CAPACITY

Runway strength data shown in this publication is derived from available information and is a realistic estimate of capability at an average level of activity. It is not intended as a maximum allowable weight or as an operating limitation. Many airport pavements are capable of supporting limited operations with gross weights in excess of the published figures. Permissible operating weights, insofar as runway strengths are concerned, are a matter of agreement between the owner and user. When desiring to operate into any airport at weights in excess of those published in the publication, users should contact the airport management for permission. Runway strength figures are shown in thousand of pounds, with the last three figures being omitted. Add 000 to figure following S, D, 2S, 2T, AUW, SWL, etc., for gross weight capacity. A blank space following the letter designator is used to indicate the runway can sustain aircraft with this type landing gear, although definite runway weight bearing capacity figures are not available, e.g., S, D. Applicable codes for typical gear configurations with S=Single, D=Dual, T=Triple and Q=Quadruple:

CURRENT	NEW	NEW DESCRIPTION
S	S	Single wheel type landing gear (DC3), (C47), (F15), etc.
D	D	Dual wheel type landing gear (BE1900), (B737), (A319), etc.
T	D	Dual wheel type landing gear (P3, C9).
ST	2S	Two single wheels in tandem type landing gear (C130).
TRT	2T	Two triple wheels in tandem type landing gear (C17), etc.
DT	2D	Two dual wheels in tandem type landing gear (B707), etc.
TT	2D	Two dual wheels in tandem type landing gear (B757, KC135).
SBTT	2D/D1	Two dual wheels in tandem/dual wheel body gear type landing gear (KC10).
None	2D/2D1	Two dual wheels in tandem/two dual wheels in tandem body gear type landing gear (A340–600).
DDT	2D/2D2	Two dual wheels in tandem/two dual wheels in double tandem body gear type landing gear (B747, E4).
TTT	3D	Three dual wheels in tandem type landing gear (B777), etc.
TT	D2	Dual wheel gear two struts per side main gear type landing gear (B52).
TDT	C5	Complex dual wheel and quadruple wheel combination landing gear (C5).

AUW—All up weight. Maximum weight bearing capacity for any aircraft irrespective of landing gear configuration.

SWL—Single Wheel Loading. (This includes information submitted in terms of Equivalent Single Wheel Loading (ESWL) and Single Isolated Wheel Loading).

PSI—Pounds per square inch. PSI is the actual figure expressing maximum pounds per square inch runway will support, e.g., (SWL 000/PSI 535).

Omission of weight bearing capacity indicates information unknown.

The ACN/PCN System is the ICAO standard method of reporting pavement strength for pavements with bearing strengths greater than 12,500 pounds. The Pavement Classification Number (PCN) is established by an engineering assessment of the runway. The PCN is for use in conjunction with an Aircraft Classification Number (ACN). Consult the Aircraft Flight Manual, Flight Information Handbook, or other appropriate source for ACN tables or charts. Currently, ACN data may not be available for all aircraft. If an ACN table or chart is available, the ACN can be calculated by taking into account the aircraft weight, the pavement type, and the subgrade category. For runways that have been evaluated under the ACN/PCN system, the PCN will be shown as a five-part code (e.g. PCN 80 R/B/W/T). Details of the coded format are as follows:

NOTE: Prior permission from the airport controlling authority is required when the ACN of the aircraft exceeds the published PCN or aircraft tire pressure exceeds the published limits.

(1) The PCN NUMBER—The reported PCN indicates that an aircraft with an ACN equal or less than the reported PCN can operate on the pavement subject to any limitation on the tire pressure.

(2) The type of pavement:
R — Rigid
F — Flexible

(3) The pavement subgrade category:
A — High
B — Medium
C — Low
D — Ultra-low

(4) The maximum tire pressure authorized for the pavement:
W — Unlimited, no pressure limit
X — High, limited to 254 psi (1.75 MPa)
Y — Medium, limited to 181 psi (1.25MPa)
Z — Low, limited to 73 psi (0.50 MPa)

(5) Pavement evaluation method:
T — Technical evaluation
U — By experience of aircraft using the pavement

RUNWAY LIGHTING

Lights are in operation sunset to sunrise. Lighting available by prior arrangement only or operating part of the night and/or pilot controlled lighting with specific operating hours are indicated under airport or military remarks. At USN/USMC facilities lights are available only during airport hours of operation. Since obstructions are usually lighted, obstruction lighting is not included in this code. Unlighted obstructions on or surrounding an airport will be noted in airport or military remarks. Runway lights nonstandard (NSTD) are systems for which the light fixtures are not FAA approved L–800 series: color, intensity, or spacing does not meet FAA standards. Nonstandard runway lights, VASI, or any other system not listed below will be shown in airport remarks or military

Legend 7. Chart Supplement.

18 AIRPORT/FACILITY DIRECTORY LEGEND

service. Temporary, emergency or limited runway edge lighting such as flares, smudge pots, lanterns or portable runway lights will also be shown in airport remarks or military service. Types of lighting are shown with the runway or runway end they serve.

NSTD—Light system fails to meet FAA standards.
LIRL—Low Intensity Runway Lights.
MIRL—Medium Intensity Runway Lights.
HIRL—High Intensity Runway Lights.
RAIL—Runway Alignment Indicator Lights.
REIL—Runway End Identifier Lights.
CL—Centerline Lights.
TDZL—Touchdown Zone Lights.
ODALS—Omni Directional Approach Lighting System.
AF OVRN—Air Force Overrun 1000´ Standard
             Approach Lighting System.
MALS—Medium Intensity Approach Lighting System.
MALSF—Medium Intensity Approach Lighting System with
             Sequenced Flashing Lights.
MALSR—Medium Intensity Approach Lighting System with
             Runway Alignment Indicator Lights.
RLLS—Runway Lead–in Light System

SALS—Short Approach Lighting System.
SALSF—Short Approach Lighting System with Sequenced
             Flashing Lights.
SSALS—Simplified Short Approach Lighting System.
SSALF—Simplified Short Approach Lighting System with
             Sequenced Flashing Lights.
SSALR—Simplified Short Approach Lighting System with
             Runway Alignment Indicator Lights.
ALSAF—High Intensity Approach Lighting System with
             Sequenced Flashing Lights.
ALSF1—High Intensity Approach Lighting System with Sequenced
             Flashing Lights, Category I, Configuration.
ALSF2—High Intensity Approach Lighting System with Sequenced
             Flashing Lights, Category II, Configuration.
SF—Sequenced Flashing Lights.
OLS—Optical Landing System.
WAVE–OFF.

NOTE: Civil ALSF2 may be operated as SSALR during favorable weather conditions. When runway edge lights are positioned more than 10 feet from the edge of the usable runway surface a remark will be added in the "Remarks" portion of the airport entry. This is applicable to Air Force, Air National Guard and Air Force Reserve Bases, and those joint use airfields on which they are tenants.

VISUAL GLIDESLOPE INDICATORS

APAP—A system of panels, which may or may not be lighted, used for alignment of approach path.

PNIL	APAP on left side of runway	PNIR	APAP on right side of runway

PAPI—Precision Approach Path Indicator

P2L	2–identical light units placed on left side of runway	P4L	4–identical light units placed on left side of runway
P2R	2–identical light units placed on right side of runway	P4R	4–identical light units placed on right side of runway

PVASI—Pulsating/steady burning visual approach slope indicator, normally a single light unit projecting two colors.

PSIL	PVASI on left side of runway	PSIR	PVASI on right side of runway

SAVASI—Simplified Abbreviated Visual Approach Slope Indicator

S2L	2–box SAVASI on left side of runway	S2R	2–box SAVASI on right side of runway

TRCV—Tri–color visual approach slope indicator, normally a single light unit projecting three colors.

TRIL	TRCV on left side of runway	TRIR	TRCV on right side of runway

VASI—Visual Approach Slope Indicator

V2L	2–box VASI on left side of runway	V6L	6–box VASI on left side of runway
V2R	2–box VASI on right side of runway	V6R	6–box VASI on right side of runway
V4L	4–box VASI on left side of runway	V12	12–box VASI on both sides of runway
V4R	4–box VASI on right side of runway	V16	16–box VASI on both sides of runway

NOTE: Approach slope angle and threshold crossing height will be shown when available; i.e., –GA 3.5° TCH 37´.

PILOT CONTROL OF AIRPORT LIGHTING

Key Mike	Function
7 times within 5 seconds	Highest intensity available
5 times within 5 seconds	Medium or lower intensity (Lower REIL or REIL–Off)
3 times within 5 seconds	Lowest intensity available (Lower REIL or REIL–Off)

Available systems will be indicated in the Service section, e.g., **LGT** ACTIVATE HIRL Rwy 07–25, MALSR Rwy 07, and VASI Rwy 07—122.8.

Where the airport is not served by an instrument approach procedure and/or has an independent type system of different specification installed by the airport sponsor, descriptions of the type lights, method of control, and operating frequency will be explained in clear text. See AIM, "Basic Flight Information and ATC Procedures," for detailed description of pilot control of airport lighting.

RUNWAY SLOPE

When available, runway slope data will be provided. Runway slope will be shown only when it is 0.3 percent or greater. On runways less than 8000 feet, the direction of the slope up will be indicated, e.g., 0.3% up NW. On runways 8000 feet or greater, the slope will be shown (up or down) on the runway end line, e.g., RWY 13: 0.3% up., RWY 31: Pole. Rgt tfc. 0.4% down.

SC, 1 FEB 20XX to 29 MAR 20XX

Legend 8. Chart Supplement.

AIRPORT/FACILITY DIRECTORY LEGEND

RUNWAY END DATA

Information pertaining to the runway approach end such as approach lights, touchdown zone lights, runway end identification lights, visual glideslope indicators, displaced thresholds, controlling obstruction, and right hand traffic pattern, will be shown on the specific runway end. "Rgt tfc"—Right traffic indicates right turns should be made on landing and takeoff for specified runway end. Runway Visual Range shall be shown as "RVR" appended with "T" for touchdown, "M" for midpoint, and "R" for rollout; e.g., RVR-TMR.

⑲ LAND AND HOLD–SHORT OPERATIONS (LAHSO)

LAHSO is an acronym for "Land and Hold–Short Operations" These operations include landing and holding short of an intersection runway, an intersecting taxiway, or other predetermined points on the runway other than a runway or taxiway. Measured distance represents the available landing distance on the landing runway, in feet.

Specific questions regarding these distances should be referred to the air traffic manager of the facility concerned. The Aeronautical Information Manual contains specific details on hold–short operations and markings.

⑳ RUNWAY DECLARED DISTANCE INFORMATION

TORA—Take-off Run Available. The length of runway declared available and suitable for the ground run of an aeroplane take–off.
TODA—Take-off Distance Available. The length of the take–off run available plus the length of the clearway, if provided.
ASDA—Accelerate–Stop Distance Available. The length of the take–off run available plus the length of the stopway, if provided.
LDA—Landing Distance Available. The length of runway which is declared available and suitable for the ground run of an aeroplane landing.

㉑ ARRESTING GEAR/SYSTEMS

Arresting gear is shown as it is located on the runway. The a–gear distance from the end of the appropriate runway (or into the overrun) is indicated in parentheses. A–Gear which has a bi–direction capability and can be utilized for emergency approach end engagement is indicated by a (B). Up to 15 minutes advance notice may be required for rigging A–Gear for approach and engagement. Airport listing may show availability of other than US Systems. This information is provided for emergency requirements only. Refer to current aircraft operating manuals for specific engagement weight and speed criteria based on aircraft structural restrictions and arresting system limitations.

Following is a list of current systems referenced in this publication identified by both Air Force and Navy terminology:

BI–DIRECTIONAL CABLE (B)

TYPE	DESCRIPTION
BAK–9	Rotary friction brake.
BAK–12A	Standard BAK–12 with 950 foot run out, 1–inch cable and 40,000 pound weight setting. Rotary friction brake.
BAK–12B	Extended BAK–12 with 1200 foot run, 1¼ inch Cable and 50,000 pounds weight setting. Rotary friction brake.
E28	Rotary Hydraulic (Water Brake).
M21	Rotary Hydraulic (Water Brake) Mobile.

The following device is used in conjunction with some aircraft arresting systems:

BAK–14	A device that raises a hook cable out of a slot in the runway surface and is remotely positioned for engagement by the tower on request. (In addition to personnel reaction time, the system requires up to five seconds to fully raise the cable.)
H	A device that raises a hook cable out of a slot in the runway surface and is remotely positioned for engagement by the tower on request. (In addition to personnel reaction time, the system requires up to one and one–half seconds to fully raise the cable.)

UNI–DIRECTIONAL CABLE

TYPE	DESCRIPTION
MB60	Textile brake—an emergency one–time use, modular braking system employing the tearing of specially woven textile straps to absorb the kinetic energy.
E5/E5–1/E5–3	Chain Type. At USN/USMC stations E–5 A–GEAR systems are rated, e.g., E–5 RATING–13R–1100 HW (DRY), 31L/R–1200 STD (WET). This rating is a function of the A–GEAR chain weight and length and is used to determine the maximum aircraft engaging speed. A dry rating applies to a stabilized surface (dry or wet) while a wet rating takes into account the amount (if any) of wet overrun that is not capable of withstanding the aircraft weight. These ratings are published under Service/Military/A-Gear in the entry.

FOREIGN CABLE

TYPE	DESCRIPTION	US EQUIVALENT
44B–3H	Rotary Hydraulic (Water Brake)	
CHAG	Chain	E–5

UNI–DIRECTIONAL BARRIER

TYPE	DESCRIPTION
MA–1A	Web barrier between stanchions attached to a chain energy absorber.
BAK–15	Web barrier between stanchions attached to an energy absorber (water squeezer, rotary friction, chain). Designed for wing engagement.

NOTE: Landing short of the runway threshold on a runway with a BAK–15 in the underrun is a significant hazard. The barrier in the down position still protrudes several inches above the underrun. Aircraft contact with the barrier short of the runway threshold can cause damage to the barrier and substantial damage to the aircraft.

OTHER

TYPE	DESCRIPTION
EMAS	Engineered Material Arresting System, located beyond the departure end of the runway, consisting of high energy absorbing materials which will crush under the weight of an aircraft.

SC, 1 FEB 20XX to 29 MAR 20XX

Legend 9. Chart Supplement.

20   AIRPORT/FACILITY DIRECTORY LEGEND

㉒ **SERVICE**

SERVICING—CIVIL

S1: Minor airframe repairs.
S2: Minor airframe and minor powerplant repairs.
S3: Major airframe and minor powerplant repairs.
S4: Major airframe and major powerplant repairs.

S5: Major airframe repairs.
S6: Minor airframe and major powerplant repairs.
S7: Major powerplant repairs.
S8: Minor powerplant repairs.

FUEL

CODE	FUEL
80	Grade 80 gasoline (Red)
100	Grade 100 gasoline (Green)
100LL	100LL gasoline (low lead) (Blue)
115	Grade 115 gasoline (115/145 military specification) (Purple)
A	Jet A, Kerosene, without FS–II*, FP** minus 40° C.
A+	Jet A, Kerosene, with FS–II*, FP** minus 40°C.
A++	Jet A, Kerosene, with FS–II*, CI/LI#, SDA##, FP** minus 40°C.
A++100	Jet A, Kerosene, with FS–II*, CI/LI#, SDA##, FP** minus 40°C, with +100 fuel additive that improves thermal stability characteristics of kerosene jet fuels.
A1	Jet A–1, Kerosene, without FS–II*, FP** minus 47°C.
A1+	Jet A–1, Kerosene with FS–II*, FP** minus 47° C.

CODE	FUEL
B	Jet B, Wide–cut, turbine fuel without FS–II*, FP** minus 50° C.
B+	Jet B, Wide–cut, turbine fuel with FS–II*, FP** minus 50° C
J4 (JP4)	(JP–4 military specification) FP** minus 58° C.
J5 (JP5)	(JP–5 military specification) Kerosene with FS–II, FP** minus 46°C.
J8 (JP8)	(JP–8 military specification) Jet A–1, Kerosene with FS–II*, CI/LI#, SDA##, FP** minus 47°C.
J8+100	(JP–8 military specification) Jet A–1, Kerosene with FS–II*, CI/LI#, SDA##, FP** minus 47°C, with +100 fuel additive that improves thermal stability characteristics of kerosene jet fuels.
J	(Jet Fuel Type Unknown)
MOGAS	Automobile gasoline which is to be used as aircraft fuel.
UL91	Unleaded Grade 91 gasoline
UL94	Unleaded Grade 94 gasoline

*(Fuel System Icing Inhibitor)   **(Freeze Point)   # (Corrosion Inhibitors/Lubricity Improvers)   ## (Static Dissipator Additive)

NOTE: Certain automobile gasoline may be used in specific aircraft engines if a FAA supplemental type certificate has been obtained. Automobile gasoline, which is to be used in aircraft engines, will be identified as "MOGAS", however, the grade/type and other octane rating will not be published.

Data shown on fuel availability represents the most recent information the publisher has been able to acquire. Because of a variety of factors, the fuel listed may not always be obtainable by transient civil pilots. Confirmation of availability of fuel should be made directly with fuel suppliers at locations where refueling is planned.

OXYGEN—CIVIL

OX 1   High Pressure
OX 2   Low Pressure

OX 3   High Pressure—Replacement Bottles
OX 4   Low Pressure—Replacement Bottles

SERVICE—MILITARY

Specific military services available at the airport are listed under this general heading. Remarks applicable to any military service are shown in the individual service listing.

JET AIRCRAFT STARTING UNITS (JASU)—MILITARY

The numeral preceding the type of unit indicates the number of units available. The absence of the numeral indicates ten or more units available. If the number of units is unknown, the number one will be shown. Absence of JASU designation indicates non–availability.

The following is a list of current JASU systems referenced in this publication:

USAF JASU (For variations in technical data, refer to T.O. 35–1–7.)
ELECTRICAL STARTING UNITS:

A/M32A–86	AC: 115/200v, 3 phase, 90 kva, 0.8 pf, 4 wire DC: 28v, 1500 amp, 72 kw (with TR pack)
MC–1A	AC: 115/208v, 400 cycle, 3 phase, 37.5 kva, 0.8 pf, 108 amp, 4 wire DC: 28v, 500 amp, 14 kw
MD–3	AC: 115/208v, 400 cycle, 3 phase, 60 kva, 0.75 pf, 4 wire DC: 28v, 1500 amp, 45 kw, split bus
MD–3A	AC: 115/208v, 400 cycle, 3 phase, 60 kva, 0.75 pf, 4 wire DC: 28v, 1500 amp, 45 kw, split bus
MD–3M	AC: 115/208v, 400 cycle, 3 phase, 60 kva, 0.75 pf, 4 wire DC: 28v, 500 amp, 15 kw
MD–4	AC: 120/208v, 400 cycle, 3 phase, 62.5 kva, 0.8 pf, 175 amp, "WYE" neutral ground, 4 wire, 120v, 400 cycle, 3 phase, 62.5 kva, 0.8 pf, 303 amp, "DELTA" 3 wire, 120v, 400 cycle, 1 phase, 62.5 kva, 0.8 pf, 520 amp, 2 wire

SC, 1 FEB 20XX to 29 MAR 20XX

Legend 10. Chart Supplement.

AIRPORT/FACILITY DIRECTORY LEGEND

AIR STARTING UNITS

AM32–95	150 +/– 5 lb/min (2055 +/– 68 cfm) at 51 +/– 2 psia
AM32A–95	150 +/– 5 lb/min @ 49 +/– 2 psia (35 +/– 2 psig)
LASS	150 +/– 5 lb/min @ 49 +/– 2 psia
MA–1A	82 lb/min (1123 cfm) at 130° air inlet temp, 45 psia (min) air outlet press
MC–1	15 cfm, 3500 psia
MC–1A	15 cfm, 3500 psia
MC–2A	15 cfm, 200 psia
MC–11	8,000 cu in cap, 4000 psig, 15 cfm

COMBINED AIR AND ELECTRICAL STARTING UNITS:

AGPU	AC: 115/200v, 400 cycle, 3 phase, 30 kw gen
	DC: 28v, 700 amp
	AIR: 60 lb/min @ 40 psig @ sea level
AM32A–60*	AIR: 120 +/– 4 lb/min (1644 +/– 55 cfm) at 49 +/– 2 psia
	AC: 120/208v, 400 cycle, 3 phase, 75 kva, 0.75 pf, 4 wire, 120v, 1 phase, 25 kva
	DC: 28v, 500 amp, 15 kw
AM32A–60A	AIR: 150 +/– 5 lb/min (2055 +/– 68 cfm at 51 +/– psia
	AC: 120/208v, 400 cycle, 3 phase, 75 kva, 0.75 pf, 4 wire
	DC: 28v, 200 amp, 5.6 kw
AM32A–60B*	AIR: 130 lb/min, 50 psia
	AC: 120/208v, 400 cycle, 3 phase, 75 kva, 0.75 pf, 4 wire
	DC: 28v, 200 amp, 5.6 kw

*NOTE: During combined air and electrical loads, the pneumatic circuitry takes preference and will limit the amount of electrical power available.

USN JASU

ELECTRICAL STARTING UNITS:

NC–8A/A1	DC: 500 amp constant, 750 amp intermittent, 28v;
	AC: 60 kva @ .8 pf, 115/200v, 3 phase, 400 Hz.
NC–10A/A1/B/C	DC: 750 amp constant, 1000 amp intermittent, 28v;
	AC: 90 kva, 115/200v, 3 phase, 400 Hz.

AIR STARTING UNITS:

GTC–85/GTE–85	120 lbs/min @ 45 psi.
MSU–200NAV/A/U47A–5	204 lbs/min @ 56 psia.
WELLS AIR START SYSTEM	180 lbs/min @ 75 psi or 120 lbs/min @ 45 psi. Simultaneous multiple start capability.

COMBINED AIR AND ELECTRICAL STARTING UNITS:

NCPP–105/RCPT	180 lbs/min @ 75 psi or 120 lbs/min @ 45 psi. 700 amp, 28v DC. 120/208v, 400 Hz AC, 30 kva.

ARMY JASU

59B2–1B	28v, 7.5 kw, 280 amp.

OTHER JASU

ELECTRICAL STARTING UNITS (DND):

CE12	AC 115/200v, 140 kva, 400 Hz, 3 phase
CE13	AC 115/200v, 60 kva, 400 Hz, 3 phase
CE14	AC/DC 115/200v, 140 kva, 400 Hz, 3 phase, 28vDC, 1500 amp
CE15	DC 22–35v, 500 amp continuous 1100 amp intermittent
CE16	DC 22–35v, 500 amp continuous 1100 amp intermittent soft start

AIR STARTING UNITS (DND):

CA2	ASA 45.5 psig, 116.4 lb/min

COMBINED AIR AND ELECTRICAL STARTING UNITS (DND)

CEA1	AC 120/208v, 60 kva, 400 Hz, 3 phase DC 28v, 75 amp
	AIR 112.5 lb/min, 47 psig

ELECTRICAL STARTING UNITS (OTHER)

C–26	28v 45kw 115–200v 15kw 380–800 Hz 1 phase 2 wire
C–26–B, C–26–C	28v 45kw: Split Bus: 115–200v 15kw 380–800 Hz 1 phase 2 wire
E3	DC 28v/10kw

AIR STARTING UNITS (OTHER):

A4	40 psi/2 lb/sec (LPAS Mk12, Mk12L, Mk12A, Mk1, Mk2B)
MA–1	150 Air HP, 115 lb/min 50 psia
MA–2	250 Air HP, 150 lb/min 75 psia

CARTRIDGE:

MXU–4A	USAF

SC, 1 FEB 20XX to 29 MAR 20XX

Legend 11. Chart Supplement.

22 AIRPORT/FACILITY DIRECTORY LEGEND

FUEL—MILITARY

Fuel available through US Military Base supply, DESC Into–Plane Contracts and/or reciprocal agreement is listed first and is followed by (Mil). At commercial airports where Into–Plane contracts are in place, the name of the refueling agent is shown. Military fuel should be used first if it is available. When military fuel cannot be obtained but Into–Plane contract fuel is available, Government aircraft must refuel with the contract fuel and applicable refueling agent to avoid any breach in contract terms and conditions. Fuel not available through the above is shown preceded by NC (no contract). When fuel is obtained from NC sources, local purchase procedures must be followed. The US Military Aircraft Identaplates DD Form 1896 (Jet Fuel), DD Form 1897 (Avgas) and AF Form 1245 (Avgas) are used at military installations only. The US Government Aviation Into–Plane Reimbursement (AIR) Card (currently issued by AVCARD) is the instrument to be used to obtain fuel under a DESC Into–Plane Contract and for NC purchases if the refueling agent at the commercial airport accepts the AVCARD. A current list of contract fuel locations is available online at https://cis.energy.dla.mil/ip_cis/. See legend item 14 for fuel code and description.

SUPPORTING FLUIDS AND SYSTEMS—MILITARY

CODE	
ADI	Anti–Detonation Injection Fluid—Reciprocating Engine Aircraft.
W	Water Thrust Augmentation—Jet Aircraft.
WAI	Water–Alcohol Injection Type, Thrust Augmentation—Jet Aircraft.
SP	Single Point Refueling.
PRESAIR	Air Compressors rated 3,000 PSI or more.
De–Ice	Anti–icing/De–icing/Defrosting Fluid (MIL–A–8243).

OXYGEN:

LPOX	Low pressure oxygen servicing.
HPOX	High pressure oxygen servicing.
LHOX	Low and high pressure oxygen servicing.
LOX	Liquid oxygen servicing.
OXRB	Oxygen replacement bottles. (Maintained primarily at Naval stations for use in acft where oxygen can be replenished only by replacement of cylinders.)
OX	Indicates oxygen servicing when type of servicing is unknown.

NOTE: Combinations of above items is used to indicate complete oxygen servicing available;

LHOXRB	Low and high pressure oxygen servicing and replacement bottles;
LPOXRB	Low pressure oxygen replacement bottles only, etc.

NOTE: Aircraft will be serviced with oxygen procured under military specifications only. Aircraft will not be serviced with medical oxygen.

NITROGEN:

LPNIT — Low pressure nitrogen servicing.

HPNIT — High pressure nitrogen servicing.

LHNIT — Low and high pressure nitrogen servicing.

OIL—MILITARY

US AVIATION OILS (MIL SPECS):

CODE	GRADE, TYPE
O–113	1065, Reciprocating Engine Oil (MIL–L–6082)
O–117	1100, Reciprocating Engine Oil (MIL–L–6082)
O–117+	1100, O–117 plus cyclohexanone (MIL–L–6082)
O–123	1065, (Dispersant), Reciprocating Engine Oil (MIL–L–22851 Type III)
O–128	1100, (Dispersant), Reciprocating Engine Oil (MIL–L–22851 Type II)
O–132	1005, Jet Engine Oil (MIL–L–6081)
O–133	1010, Jet Engine Oil (MIL–L–6081)
O–147	None, MIL–L–6085A Lubricating Oil, Instrument, Synthetic
O–148	None, MIL–L–7808 (Synthetic Base) Turbine Engine Oil
O–149	None, Aircraft Turbine Engine Synthetic, 7.5c St
O–155	None, MIL–L–6086C, Aircraft, Medium Grade
O–156	None, MIL–L–23699 (Synthetic Base), Turboprop and Turboshaft Engines
JOAP/SOAP	Joint Oil Analysis Program. JOAP support is furnished during normal duty hours, other times on request. (JOAP and SOAP programs provide essentially the same service, JOAP is now the standard joint service supported program.)

TRANSIENT ALERT (TRAN ALERT)—MILITARY

Tran Alert service is considered to include all services required for normal aircraft turn–around, e.g., servicing (fuel, oil, oxygen, etc.), debriefing to determine requirements for maintenance, minor maintenance, inspection and parking assistance of transient aircraft. Drag chute repack, specialized maintenance, or extensive repairs will be provided within the capabilities and priorities of the base. Delays can be anticipated after normal duty hours/holidays/weekends regardless of the hours of transient maintenance operation. Pilots should not expect aircraft to be serviced for TURN–AROUNDS during time periods when servicing or maintenance manpower is not available. In the case of airports not operated exclusively by US military, the servicing indicated by the remarks will not always be available for US military aircraft. When transient alert services are not shown, facilities are unknown. NO PRIORITY BASIS—means that transient alert services will be provided only after all the requirements for mission/tactical assigned aircraft have been accomplished.

SC, 1 FEB 20XX to 29 MAR 20XX

Legend 12. Chart Supplement.

AIRPORT/FACILITY DIRECTORY LEGEND

㉓ AIRPORT REMARKS

The Attendance Schedule is the months, days and hours the airport is actually attended. Airport attendance does not mean watchman duties or telephone accessibility, but rather an attendant or operator on duty to provide at least minimum services (e.g., repairs, fuel, transportation).

Airport Remarks have been grouped in order of applicability. Airport remarks are limited to those items of information that are determined essential for operational use, i.e., conditions of a permanent or indefinite nature and conditions that will remain in effect for more than 30 days concerning aeronautical facilities, services, maintenance available, procedures or hazards, knowledge of which is essential for safe and efficient operation of aircraft. Information concerning permanent closing of a runway or taxiway will not be shown. A note "See Special Notices" shall be applied within this remarks section when a special notice applicable to the entry is contained in the Special Notices section of this publication.

Parachute Jumping indicates parachute jumping areas associated with the airport. See Parachute Jumping Area section of this publication for additional Information.

Landing Fee indicates landing charges for private or non—revenue producing aircraft. In addition, fees may be charged for planes that remain over a couple of hours and buy no services, or at major airline terminals for all aircraft.

Note: Unless otherwise stated, remarks including runway ends refer to the runway's approach end.

㉔ MILITARY REMARKS

Joint Civil/Military airports contain both Airport Remarks and Military Remarks. Military Remarks published for these airports are applicable only to the military. Military and joint Military/Civil airports contain only Military Remarks. Remarks contained in this section may not be applicable to civil users. When both sets of remarks exist, the first set is applicable to the primary operator of the airport. Remarks applicable to a tenant on the airport are shown preceded by the tenant organization, i.e., (A) (AF) (N) (ANG), etc. Military airports operate 24 hours unless otherwise specified. Airport operating hours are listed first (airport operating hours will only be listed if they are different than the airport attended hours or if the attended hours are unavailable) followed by pertinent remarks in order of applicability. Remarks will include information on restrictions, hazards, traffic pattern, noise abatement, customs/agriculture/immigration, and miscellaneous information applicable to the Military.

Type of restrictions:

CLOSED: When designated closed, the airport is restricted from use by all aircraft unless stated otherwise. Any closure applying to specific type of aircraft or operation will be so stated. USN/USMC/USAF airports are considered closed during non—operating hours. Closed airports may be utilized during an emergency provided there is a safe landing area.

OFFICIAL BUSINESS ONLY: The airfield is closed to all transient military aircraft for obtaining routine services such as fueling, passenger drop off or pickup, practice approaches, parking, etc. The airfield may be used by aircrews and aircraft if official government business (including civilian) must be conducted on or near the airfield and prior permission is received from the airfield manager.

AF OFFICIAL BUSINESS ONLY OR NAVY OFFICIAL BUSINESS ONLY: Indicates that the restriction applies only to service indicated.

PRIOR PERMISSION REQUIRED (PPR): Airport is closed to transient aircraft unless approval for operation is obtained from the appropriate commander through Chief, Airfield Management or Airfield Operations Officer. Official Business or PPR does not preclude the use of US Military airports as an alternate for IFR flights. If a non—US military airport is used as a weather alternate and requires a PPR, the PPR must be requested and confirmed before the flight departs. The purpose of PPR is to control volume and flow of traffic rather than to prohibit it. Prior permission is required for all aircraft requiring transient alert service outside the published transient alert duty hours. All aircraft carrying hazardous materials must obtain prior permission as outlined in AFJI 11–204, AR 95–27, OPNAVINST 3710.7.

Note: OFFICIAL BUSINESS ONLY AND PPR restrictions are not applicable to Special Air Mission (SAM) or Special Air Resource (SPAR) aircraft providing person or persons on aboard are designated Code 6 or higher as explained in AFJMAN 11–213, AR 95–11, OPNAVINST 3722–8J. Official Business Only or PPR do not preclude the use of the airport as an alternate for IFR flights.

㉕ AIRPORT MANAGER

The phone number of the airport manager.

㉖ WEATHER DATA SOURCES

Weather data sources will be listed alphabetically followed by their assigned frequencies and/or telephone number and hours of operation.

ASOS—Automated Surface Observing System. Reports the same as an AWOS–3 plus precipitation identification and intensity, and freezing rain occurrence;

AWOS—Automated Weather Observing System

AWOS–A—reports altimeter setting (all other information is advisory only).

AWOS–AV—reports altimeter and visibility.

AWOS–1—reports altimeter setting, wind data and usually temperature, dew point and density altitude.

AWOS–2—reports the same as AWOS–1 plus visibility.

AWOS–3—reports the same as AWOS–1 plus visibility and cloud/ceiling data.

AWOS–3P reports the same as the AWOS–3 system, plus a precipitation identification sensor.

AWOS–3PT reports the same as the AWOS–3 system, plus precipitation identification sensor and a thunderstorm/lightning reporting capability.

Legend 13. Chart Supplement.

24 AIRPORT/FACILITY DIRECTORY LEGEND

AWOS-3T reports the same as AWOS-3 system and includes a thunderstorm/lightning reporting capability.

See AIM, Basic Flight Information and ATC Procedures for detailed description of Weather Data Sources.

AWOS-4—reports same as AWOS-3 system, plus precipitation occurrence, type and accumulation, freezing rain, thunderstorm and runway surface sensors.

HIWAS—See RADIO AIDS TO NAVIGATION

LAWRS—Limited Aviation Weather Reporting Station where observers report cloud height, weather, obstructions to vision, temperature and dewpoint (in most cases), surface wind, altimeter and pertinent remarks.

LLWAS—indicates a Low Level Wind Shear Alert System consisting of a center field and several field perimeter anemometers.

SAWRS—identifies airports that have a Supplemental Aviation Weather Reporting Station available to pilots for current weather information.

SWSL—Supplemental Weather Service Location providing current local weather information via radio and telephone.

TDWR—indicates airports that have Terminal Doppler Weather Radar.

WSP—indicates airports that have Weather System Processor.

When the automated weather source is broadcast over an associated airport NAVAID frequency (see NAVAID line), it shall be indicated by a bold ASOS, AWOS, or HIWAS followed by the frequency, identifier and phone number, if available.

㉗ COMMUNICATIONS

Airport terminal control facilities and radio communications associated with the airport shall be shown. When the call sign is not the same as the airport name the call sign will be shown. Frequencies shall normally be shown in descending order with the primary frequency listed first. Frequencies will be listed, together with sectorization indicated by outbound radials, and hours of operation. Communications will be listed in sequence as follows:

Single Frequency Approach (SFA), Common Traffic Advisory Frequency (CTAF), Aeronautical Advisory Stations (UNICOM) or (AUNICOM), and Automatic Terminal Information Service (ATIS) along with their frequency is shown, where available, on the line following the heading "COMMUNICATIONS." When the CTAF and UNICOM frequencies are the same, the frequency will be shown as CTAF/UNICOM 122.8.

The FSS telephone nationwide is toll free 1–800–WX–BRIEF (1–800–992–7433). When the FSS is located on the field it will be indicated as "on arpt". Frequencies available at the FSS will follow in descending order. Remote Communications Outlet (RCO) providing service to the airport followed by the frequency and FSS RADIO name will be shown when available. FSS's provide information on airport conditions, radio aids and other facilities, and process flight plans. Airport Advisory Service (AAS) is provided on the CTAF by FSS's for select non–tower airports or airports where the tower is not in operation.

(See AIM, Para 4–1–9 Traffic Advisory Practices at Airports Without Operating Control Towers or AC 90–42C.)

Aviation weather briefing service is provided by FSS specialists. Flight and weather briefing services are also available by calling the telephone numbers listed.

Remote Communications Outlet (RCO)—An unmanned air/ground communications facility that is remotely controlled and provides UHF or VHF communications capability to extend the service range of an FSS.

Civil Communications Frequencies–Civil communications frequencies used in the FSS air/ground system are operated on 122.0, 122.2, 123.6; emergency 121.5; plus receive–only on 122.1.

    a. 122.0 is assigned as the Enroute Flight Advisory Service frequency at selected FSS RADIO outlets.

    b. 122.2 is assigned as a common enroute frequency.

    c. 123.6 is assigned as the airport advisory frequency at select non–tower locations. At airports with a tower, FSS may provide airport advisories on the tower frequency when tower is closed.

    d. 122.1 is the primary receive–only frequency at VOR's.

    e. Some FSS's are assigned 50 kHz frequencies in the 122–126 MHz band (eg. 122.45). Pilots using the FSS A/G system should refer to this directory or appropriate charts to determine frequencies available at the FSS or remoted facility through which they wish to communicate.

Emergency frequency 121.5 and 243.0 are available at all Flight Service Stations, most Towers, Approach Control and RADAR facilities.

Frequencies published followed by the letter "T" or "R", indicate that the facility will only transmit or receive respectively on that frequency. All radio aids to navigation (NAVAID) frequencies are transmit only. In cases where communications frequencies are annotated with (R) or (E), (R) indicates Radar Capability and (E) indicates Emergency Frequency.

TERMINAL SERVICES

SFA—Single Frequency Approach.

CTAF—A program designed to get all vehicles and aircraft at airports without an operating control tower on a common frequency.

ATIS—A continuous broadcast of recorded non–control information in selected terminal areas.

D–ATIS—Digital ATIS provides ATIS information in text form outside the standard reception range of conventional ATIS via landline & data link communications and voice message within range of existing transmitters.

AUNICOM—Automated UNICOM is a computerized, command response system that provides automated weather, radio check capability and airport advisory information selected from an automated menu by microphone clicks.

UNICOM—A non–government air/ground radio communications facility which may provide airport information.

PTD—Pilot to Dispatcher.

APP CON—Approach Control. The symbol ⓡ indicates radar approach control.

TOWER—Control tower.

GCA—Ground Control Approach System.

GND CON—Ground Control.

SC, 1 FEB 20XX to 29 MAR 20XX

Legend 14. Chart Supplement.

AIRPORT/FACILITY DIRECTORY LEGEND 25

GCO—Ground Communication Outlet—An unstaffed, remotely controlled, ground/ground communications facility. Pilots at uncontrolled airports may contact ATC and FSS via VHF to a telephone connection to obtain an instrument clearance or close a VFR or IFR flight plan. They may also get an updated weather briefing prior to takeoff. Pilots will use four "key clicks" on the VHF radio to contact the appropriate ATC facility or six "key clicks" to contact the FSS. The GCO system is intended to be used only on the ground.

DEP CON—Departure Control. The symbol ℝ indicates radar departure control.

CLNC DEL—Clearance Delivery.

CPDLC—Controller Pilot Data Link Communication. FANS ATC data communication capability from the aircraft to the ATC Data Link system.

PRE TAXI CLNC—Pre taxi clearance.

VFR ADVSY SVC—VFR Advisory Service. Service provided by Non–Radar Approach Control.
    Advisory Service for VFR aircraft (upon a workload basis) ctc APP CON.

COMD POST—Command Post followed by the operator call sign in parenthesis.

PMSV—Pilot–to–Metro Service call sign, frequency and hours of operation, when full service is other than continuous. PMSV installations at which weather observation service is available shall be indicated, following the frequency and/or hours of operation as "Wx obsn svc 1900–0000Z‡" or "other times" may be used when no specific time is given. PMSV facilities manned by forecasters are considered "Full Service". PMSV facilities manned by weather observers are listed as "Limited Service".

OPS—Operations followed by the operator call sign in parenthesis.

CON

RANGE

FLT FLW—Flight Following

MEDIVAC

NOTE: Communication frequencies followed by the letter "X" indicate frequency available on request.

⑳ **AIRSPACE**

Information concerning Class B, C, and part–time D and E surface area airspace shall be published with effective times, if available.

CLASS B—Radar Sequencing and Separation Service for all aircraft in CLASS B airspace.

CLASS C—Separation between IFR and VFR aircraft and sequencing of VFR arrivals to the primary airport.

TRSA—Radar Sequencing and Separation Service for participating VFR Aircraft within a Terminal Radar Service Area.

Class C, D, and E airspace described in this publication is that airspace usually consisting of a 5 NM radius core surface area that begins at the surface and extends upward to an altitude above the airport elevation (charted in MSL for Class C and Class D). Class E surface airspace normally extends from the surface up to but not including the overlying controlled airspace.

When part–time Class C or Class D airspace defaults to Class E, the core surface area becomes Class E. This will be formatted as:
AIRSPACE: CLASS C svc "times" ctc **APP CON** other times CLASS E:
or
AIRSPACE: CLASS D svc "times" other times CLASS E.

When a part–time Class C, Class D or Class E surface area defaults to Class G, the core surface area becomes Class G up to, but not including, the overlying controlled airspace. Normally, the overlying controlled airspace is Class E airspace beginning at either 700´ or 1200´ AGL and may be determined by consulting the relevant VFR Sectional or Terminal Area Charts. This will be formatted as:
AIRSPACE: CLASS C svc "times" ctc **APP CON** other times CLASS G, with CLASS E 700´ (or 1200´) AGL & abv:
or
AIRSPACE: CLASS D svc "times" other times CLASS G with CLASS E 700´ (or 1200´) AGL & abv:
or
AIRSPACE: CLASS E svc "times" other times CLASS G with CLASS E 700´ (or 1200´) AGL & abv.

NOTE: AIRSPACE SVC "TIMES" INCLUDE ALL ASSOCIATED ARRIVAL EXTENSIONS. Surface area arrival extensions for instrument approach procedures become part of the primary core surface area. These extensions may be either Class D or Class E airspace and are effective concurrent with the times of the primary core surface area. For example, when a part–time Class C, Class D or Class E surface area defaults to Class G, the associated arrival extensions will default to Class G at the same time. When a part–time Class C or Class D surface area defaults to Class E, the arrival extensions will remain in effect as Class E airspace.

NOTE: CLASS E AIRSPACE EXTENDING UPWARD FROM 700 FEET OR MORE ABOVE THE SURFACE, DESIGNATED IN CONJUNCTION WITH AN AIRPORT WITH AN APPROVED INSTRUMENT PROCEDURE.
Class E 700´ AGL (shown as magenta vignette on sectional charts) and 1200´ AGL (blue vignette) areas are designated when necessary to provide controlled airspace for transitioning to/from the terminal and enroute environments. Unless otherwise specified, these 700´/1200´ AGL Class E airspace areas remain in effect continuously, regardless of airport operating hours or surface area status. These transition areas should not be confused with surface areas or arrival extensions.

(See Chapter 3, AIRSPACE, in the Aeronautical Information Manual for further details)

Legend 15. Chart Supplement.

26 AIRPORT/FACILITY DIRECTORY LEGEND

㉙ **VOR TEST FACILITY (VOT)**

The VOT transmits a signal which provided users a convenient means to determine the operational status and accuracy of an aircraft VOR receiver while on the ground. Ground based VOTs and the associated frequency shall be shown when available. VOTs are also shown with identifier, frequency and referenced remarks in the VOR Receiver Check section in the back of this publication.

㉚ **RADIO AIDS TO NAVIGATION**

The Airport/Facility Directory section of the Chart Supplement lists, by facility name, all Radio Aids to Navigation that appear on FAA, Aeronautical Information Services Visual or IFR Aeronautical Charts and those upon which the FAA has approved an Instrument Approach Procedure, with exception of selected TACANs. All VOR, VORTAC, TACAN and ILS equipment in the National Airspace System has an automatic monitoring and shutdown feature in the event of malfunction. Unmonitored, as used in this publication, for any navigational aid, means that monitoring personnel cannot observe the malfunction or shutdown signal. The NAVAID NOTAM file identifier will be shown as "NOTAM FILE IAD" and will be listed on the Radio Aids to Navigation line. When two or more NAVAIDS are listed and the NOTAM file identifier is different from that shown on the Radio Aids to Navigation line, it will be shown with the NAVAID listing. NOTAM file identifiers for ILSs and its components (e.g., NDB (LOM) are the same as the associated airports and are not repeated. Automated Surface Observing System (ASOS), Automated Weather Observing System (AWOS), and Hazardous Inflight Weather Advisory Service (HIWAS) will be shown when this service is broadcast over selected NAVAIDs.

NAVAID information is tabulated as indicated in the following sample:

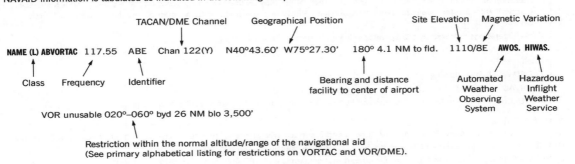

Note: Those DME channel numbers with a (Y) suffix require TACAN to be placed in the "Y" mode to receive distance information.

HIWAS—Hazardous Inflight Weather Advisory Service is a continuous broadcast of inflight weather advisories including summarized SIGMETs, convective SIGMETs, AIRMETs and urgent PIREPs. HIWAS is presently broadcast over selected VOR's throughout the U.S.

ASR/PAR—Indicates that Surveillance (ASR) or Precision (PAR) radar instrument approach minimums are published in the U.S. Terminal Procedures. Only part–time hours of operation will be shown.

SC, 1 FEB 20XX to 29 MAR 20XX

Legend 16. Chart Supplement.

Appendix 2

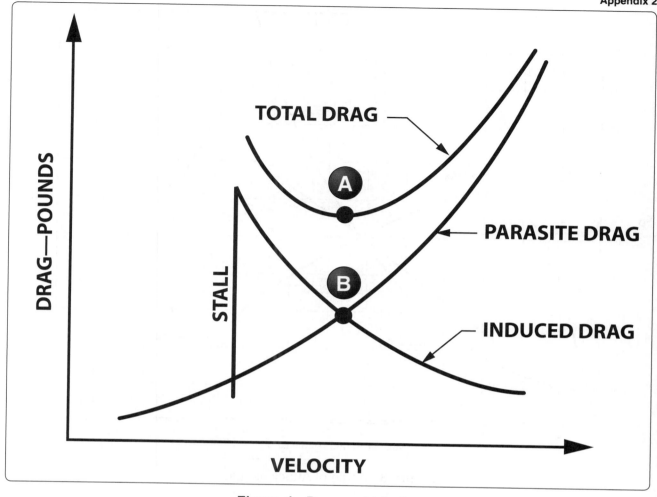

Figure 1. Drag vs. Velocity.

GROSS WEIGHT 2,750 LB			ANGLE OF BANK			
			LEVEL	30°	45°	60°
POWER			GEAR AND FLAPS UP			
ON	MPH		62	67	74	88
	KTS		54	58	64	76
OFF	MPH		75	81	89	106
	KTS		65	70	77	92
			GEAR AND FLAPS DOWN			
ON	MPH		54	58	64	76
	KTS		47	50	56	66
OFF	MPH		66	71	78	93
	KTS		57	62	68	81

Figure 2. Stall Speeds.

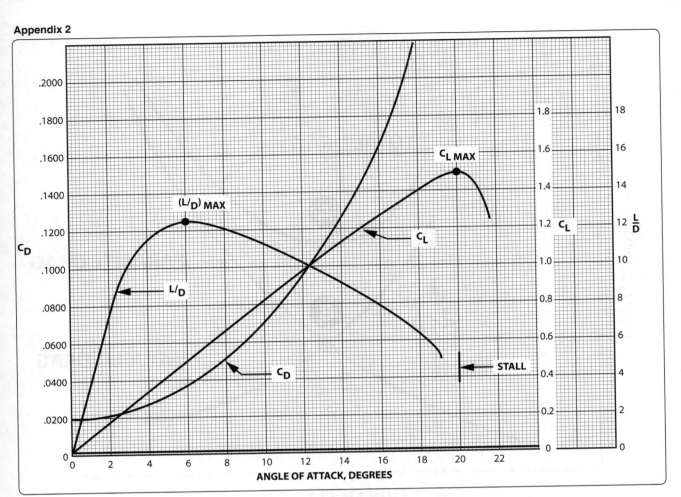

Figure 3. Angle of Attack vs. Lift.

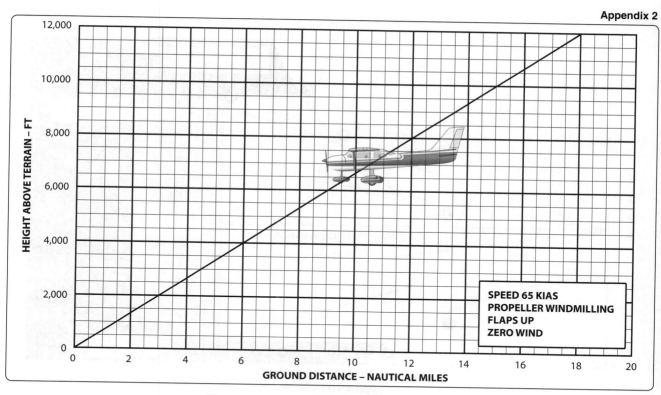

Figure 3A. Maximum Glide Distance.

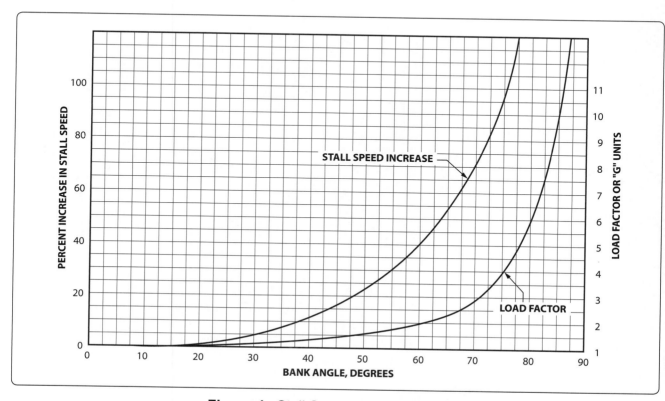

Figure 4. Stall Speed vs. Load Factor.

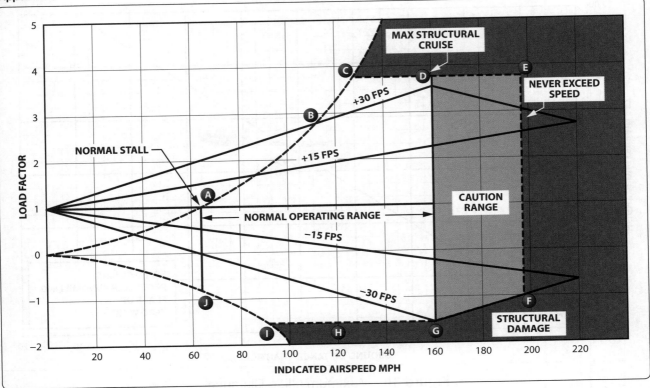

Figure 5. Velocity vs. Load Factor.

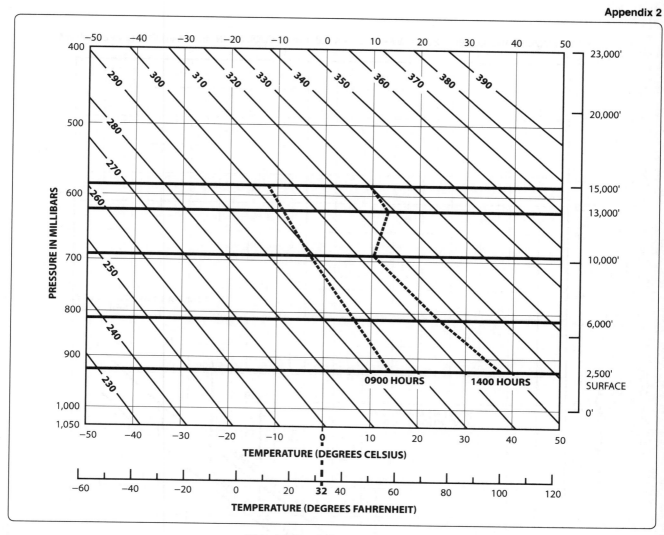

Figure 6. Adiabatic Chart.

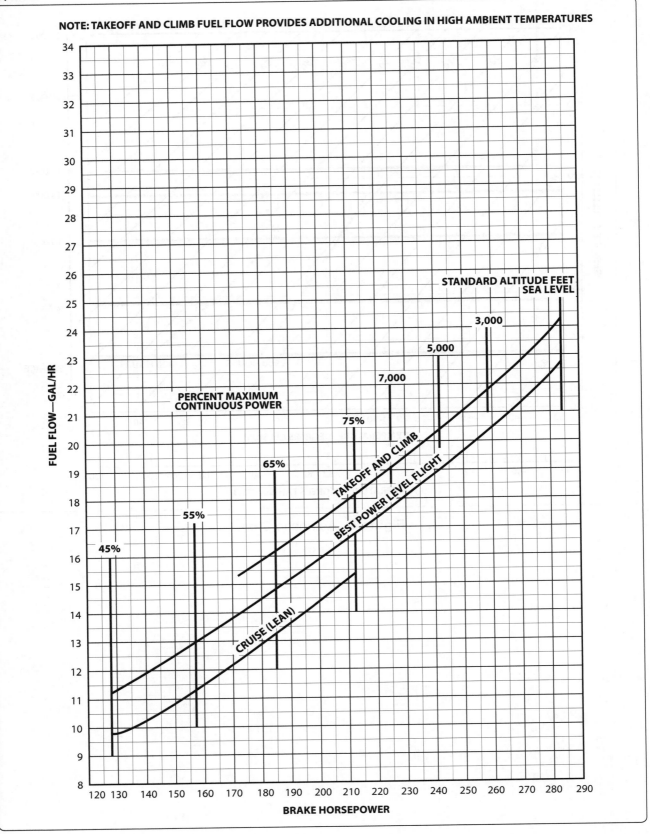

Figure 8. Fuel Consumption vs. Brake Horsepower.

NORMAL CLIMB—100 KIAS

CONDITIONS:
FLAPS UP
GEAR UP
2,550 RPM
25 INCHES MP OR FULL THROTTLE
COWL FLAPS OPEN
STANDARD TEMPERATURE

MIXTURE SETTING	
PRESS ALT	PPH
S.L. to 4,000	108
8,000	96
12,000	84

NOTES:
1. INCREASE TIME, FUEL, AND DISTANCE BY 10% FOR EACH 10 °C ABOVE STANDARD TEMPERATURE.
2. ADD 12 POUNDS OF FUEL FOR ENGINE START, TAXI, AND TAKEOFF ALLOWANCE.
3. DISTANCES SHOWN ARE BASED ON ZERO WIND.

WEIGHT (LB)	PRESS ALT (FT)	RATE OF CLIMB (FPM)	FROM SEA LEVEL		
			TIME (MIN)	FUEL USED (LB)	DISTANCE (NM)
3,800	S.L.	580	0	0	0
	2,000	580	3	6	6
	4,000	570	7	12	12
	6,000	470	11	19	19
	8,000	365	16	27	28
	10,000	265	22	37	40
	12,000	165	32	51	59
3,500	S.L.	685	0	0	0
	2,000	685	3	5	5
	4,000	675	6	11	10
	6,000	565	9	16	16
	8,000	455	13	23	23
	10,000	350	18	31	33
	12,000	240	25	41	46
3,200	S.L.	800	0	0	0
	2,000	800	2	4	4
	4,000	795	5	9	8
	6,000	675	8	14	13
	8,000	560	11	19	19
	10,000	445	15	25	27
	12,000	325	20	33	37

Figure 9. Fuel, Time, and Distance to Climb.

MAXIMUM RATE OF CLIMB

CONDITIONS:
FLAPS UP
GEAR UP
2,700 RPM
FULL THROTTLE
MIXTURE SET AT PLACARD FUEL FLOW
COWL FLAPS OPEN
STANDARD TEMPERATURE

MIXTURE SETTING	
PRESS ALT	PPH
S.L.	138
4,000	126
8,000	114
12,000	102

NOTES:
1. ADD 12 POUNDS OF FUEL FOR ENGINE START, TAXI, AND TAKEOFF ALLOWANCE.
2. INCREASE TIME, FUEL, AND DISTANCE BY 10% FOR EACH 10 °C ABOVE STANDARD TEMPERATURE.
3. DISTANCES SHOWN ARE BASED ON ZERO WIND.

WEIGHT (LB)	PRESS ALT (FT)	CLIMB SPEED (KIAS)	RATE OF CLIMB (FPM)	FROM SEA LEVEL		
				TIME (MIN)	FUEL USED (LB)	DISTANCE (NM)
3,800	S.L.	97	860	0	0	0
	2,000	95	760	2	6	4
	4,000	94	660	5	12	9
	6,000	93	565	9	18	14
	8,000	91	465	13	26	21
	10,000	90	365	18	35	29
	12,000	89	265	24	47	41
3,500	S.L.	95	990	0	0	0
	2,000	94	885	2	5	3
	4,000	93	780	5	10	7
	6,000	91	675	7	16	12
	8,000	90	570	11	22	17
	10,000	89	465	15	29	24
	12,000	87	360	20	38	32
3,200	S.L.	94	1,135	0	0	0
	2,000	92	1,020	2	4	3
	4,000	91	910	4	9	6
	6,000	90	800	6	14	10
	8,000	88	685	9	19	14
	10,000	87	575	12	25	20
	12,000	86	465	16	32	26

Figure 10. Fuel, Time, and Distance to Climb.

GROSS WEIGHT – 2,300 LB
STANDARD CONDITIONS
ZERO WIND LEAN MIXTURE

NOTE: MAXIMUM CRUISE IS NORMALLY LIMITED TO 75% POWER.

ALT.	RPM	% BHP	TAS MPH	GAL/ HOUR	38 GAL (NO RESERVE)		48 GAL (NO RESERVE)	
					ENDR (HOURS)	RANGE (MILES)	ENDR (HOURS)	RANGE (MILES)
2,500	2,700	86	134	9.7	3.9	525	4.9	660
	2,600	79	129	8.6	4.4	570	5.6	720
	2,500	72	123	7.8	4.9	600	6.2	760
	2,400	65	117	7.2	5.3	620	6.7	780
	2,300	58	111	6.7	5.7	630	7.2	795
	2,200	52	103	6.3	6.1	625	7.7	790
5,000	2,700	82	134	9.0	4.2	565	5.3	710
	2,600	75	128	8.1	4.7	600	5.9	760
	2,500	68	122	7.4	5.1	625	6.4	790
	2,400	61	116	6.9	5.5	635	6.9	805
	2,300	55	108	6.5	5.9	635	7.4	805
	2,200	49	100	6.0	6.3	630	7.9	795
7,500	2,700	78	133	8.4	4.5	600	5.7	755
	2,600	71	127	7.7	4.9	625	6.2	790
	2,500	64	121	7.1	5.3	645	6.7	810
	2,400	58	113	6.7	5.7	645	7.2	820
	2,300	52	105	6.2	6.1	640	7.7	810
10,000	2,650	70	129	7.6	5.0	640	6.3	810
	2,600	67	125	7.3	5.2	650	6.5	820
	2,500	61	118	6.9	5.5	655	7.0	830
	2,400	55	110	6.4	5.9	650	7.5	825
	2,300	49	100	6.0	6.3	635	8.0	800

Figure 11. Cruise and Range Performance.

PRESSURE ALTITUDE – 18,000 FEET

CONDITIONS:
4,000 POUNDS
RECOMMENDED LEAN MIXTURE
COWL FLAPS CLOSED

NOTES:
FOR BEST FUEL ECONOMY AT 70% POWER OR LESS, OPERATE AT 6 PPH LEANER THAN SHOWN IN THIS CHART OR AT PEAK EGT.

RPM	MP	20 °C BELOW STANDARD TEMPERATURE −41 °C			STANDARD TEMPERATURE −21 °C			20 °C ABOVE STANDARD TEMP −1 °C		
		% BHP	KTAS	PPH	% BHP	KTAS	PPH	% BHP	KTAS	PPH
2,500	30	---	---	---	81	188	106	76	185	100
	28	80	184	105	76	182	99	71	178	93
	26	75	178	99	71	176	93	67	172	88
	24	70	171	91	66	168	86	62	164	81
	22	63	162	84	60	159	79	56	155	75
2,400	30	81	185	107	77	183	101	72	180	94
	28	76	179	100	72	177	94	67	173	88
	26	71	172	93	67	170	88	63	166	83
	24	66	165	87	62	163	82	58	159	77
	22	61	158	80	57	155	76	54	150	72
2,300	30	79	182	103	74	180	97	70	176	91
	28	74	176	97	70	174	91	65	170	86
	26	69	170	91	65	167	86	61	163	81
	24	64	162	84	60	159	79	56	155	75
	22	58	154	77	55	150	73	51	145	65
2,200	26	66	166	87	62	163	82	58	159	77
	24	61	158	80	57	154	76	54	150	72
	22	55	148	73	51	144	69	48	138	66
	20	49	136	66	46	131	63	43	124	59

Figure 12. Cruise Performance.

MAXIMUM RATE OF CLIMB

CONDITIONS:
FLAPS UP
GEAR UP
2,600 RPM
COWL FLAPS OPEN
STANDARD TEMPERATURE

MIXTURE SETTING		
PRESS ALT	MP	PPH
S.L. TO 17,000	35	162
18,000	34	156
20,000	32	144
22,000	30	132
24,000	28	120

NOTES:
1. ADD 16 POUNDS OF FUEL FOR ENGINE START, TAXI, AND TAKEOFF ALLOWANCE.
2. INCREASE TIME, FUEL, AND DISTANCE BY 10% FOR EACH 10 °C ABOVE STANDARD TEMPERATURE.
3. DISTANCES SHOWN ARE BASED ON ZERO WIND.

WEIGHT (LB)	PRESS ALT (FT)	CLIMB SPEED (KIAS)	RATE OF CLIMB (FPM)	FROM SEA LEVEL		
				TIME (MIN)	FUEL USED (LB)	DISTANCE (NM)
4,000	S.L.	100	930	0	0	0
	4,000	100	890	4	12	7
	8,000	100	845	9	24	16
	12,000	100	790	14	38	25
	16,000	100	720	19	52	36
	20,000	99	515	26	69	50
	24,000	97	270	37	92	74
3,700	S.L.	99	1,060	0	0	0
	4,000	99	1,020	4	10	6
	8,000	99	975	8	21	13
	12,000	99	915	12	33	21
	16,000	99	845	17	45	30
	20,000	97	630	22	59	42
	24,000	95	370	30	77	60
3,400	S.L.	97	1,205	0	0	0
	4,000	97	1,165	3	9	5
	8,000	97	1,120	7	19	12
	12,000	97	1,060	11	29	18
	16,000	97	985	15	39	26
	20,000	96	760	19	51	36
	24,000	94	485	26	65	50

Figure 13. Fuel, Time, and Distance to Climb.

NORMAL CLIMB – 110 KIAS

CONDITIONS:
FLAPS UP
GEAR UP
2,500 RPM
30 INCHES HG
120 PPH FUEL FLOW
COWL FLAPS OPEN
STANDARD TEMPERATURE

NOTES:
1. ADD 16 POUNDS OF FUEL FOR ENGINE START, TAXI, AND TAKEOFF ALLOWANCE.
2. INCREASE TIME, FUEL, AND DISTANCE BY 10% FOR EACH 7 °C ABOVE STANDARD TEMPERATURE.
3. DISTANCES SHOWN ARE BASED ON ZERO WIND.

WEIGHT (LB)	PRESS ALT (FT)	RATE OF CLIMB (FPM)	FROM SEA LEVEL		
			TIME (MIN)	FUEL USED (LB)	DISTANCE (NM)
4,000	S.L.	605	0	0	0
	4,000	570	7	14	13
	8,000	530	14	28	27
	12,000	485	22	44	43
	16,000	430	31	62	63
	20,000	365	41	82	87
3,700	S.L.	700	0	0	0
	4,000	665	6	12	11
	8,000	625	12	24	23
	12,000	580	19	37	37
	16,000	525	26	52	53
	20,000	460	34	68	72
3,400	S.L.	810	0	0	0
	4,000	775	5	10	9
	8,000	735	10	21	20
	12,000	690	16	32	31
	16,000	635	22	44	45
	20,000	565	29	57	61

Figure 14. Fuel, Time, and Distance to Climb.

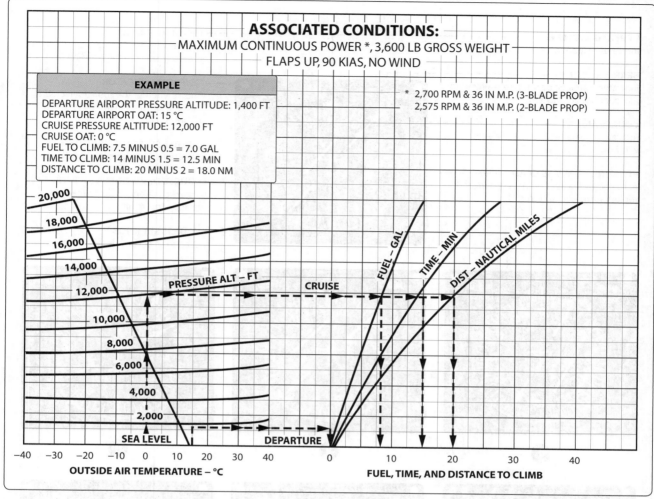

Figure 15. Fuel, Time, and Distance to Climb.

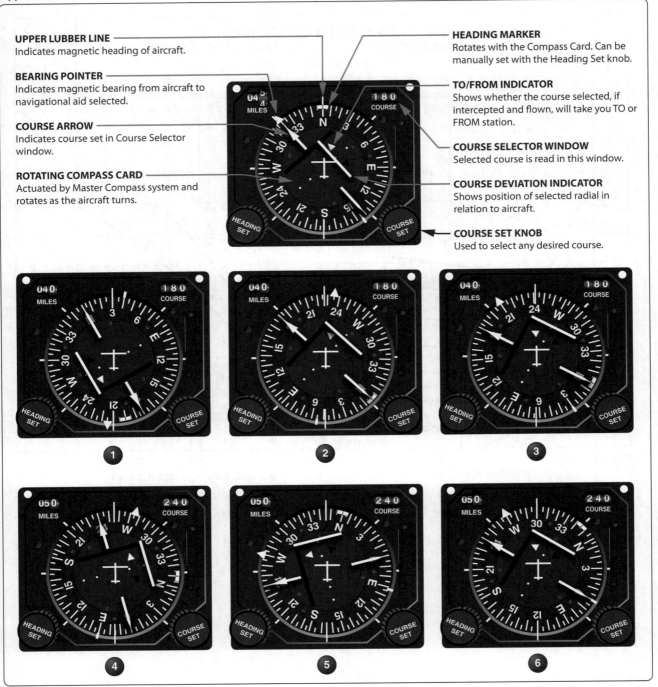

UPPER LUBBER LINE
Indicates magnetic heading of aircraft.

BEARING POINTER
Indicates magnetic bearing from aircraft to navigational aid selected.

COURSE ARROW
Indicates course set in Course Selector window.

ROTATING COMPASS CARD
Actuated by Master Compass system and rotates as the aircraft turns.

HEADING MARKER
Rotates with the Compass Card. Can be manually set with the Heading Set knob.

TO/FROM INDICATOR
Shows whether the course selected, if intercepted and flown, will take you TO or FROM station.

COURSE SELECTOR WINDOW
Selected course is read in this window.

COURSE DEVIATION INDICATOR
Shows position of selected radial in relation to aircraft.

COURSE SET KNOB
Used to select any desired course.

Figure 17. Horizontal Situation Indicator (HSI).

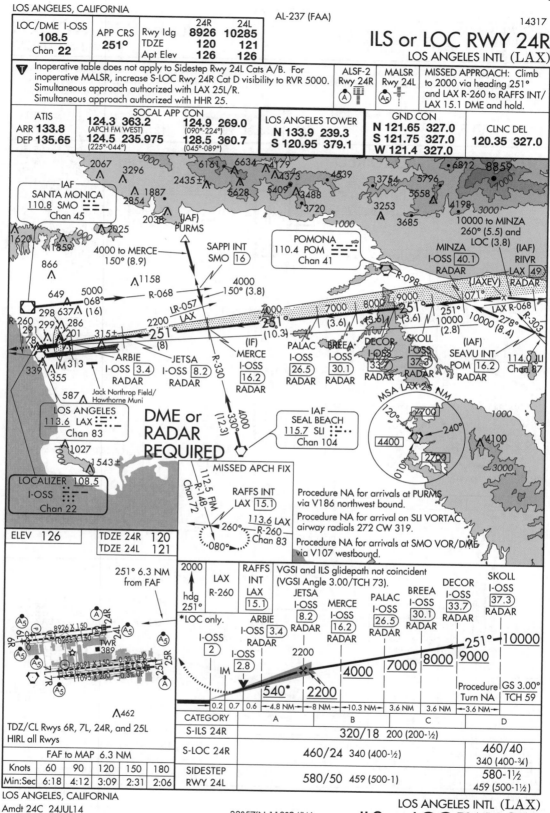

Figure 26. ILS or LOC RWY 24R (LAX).

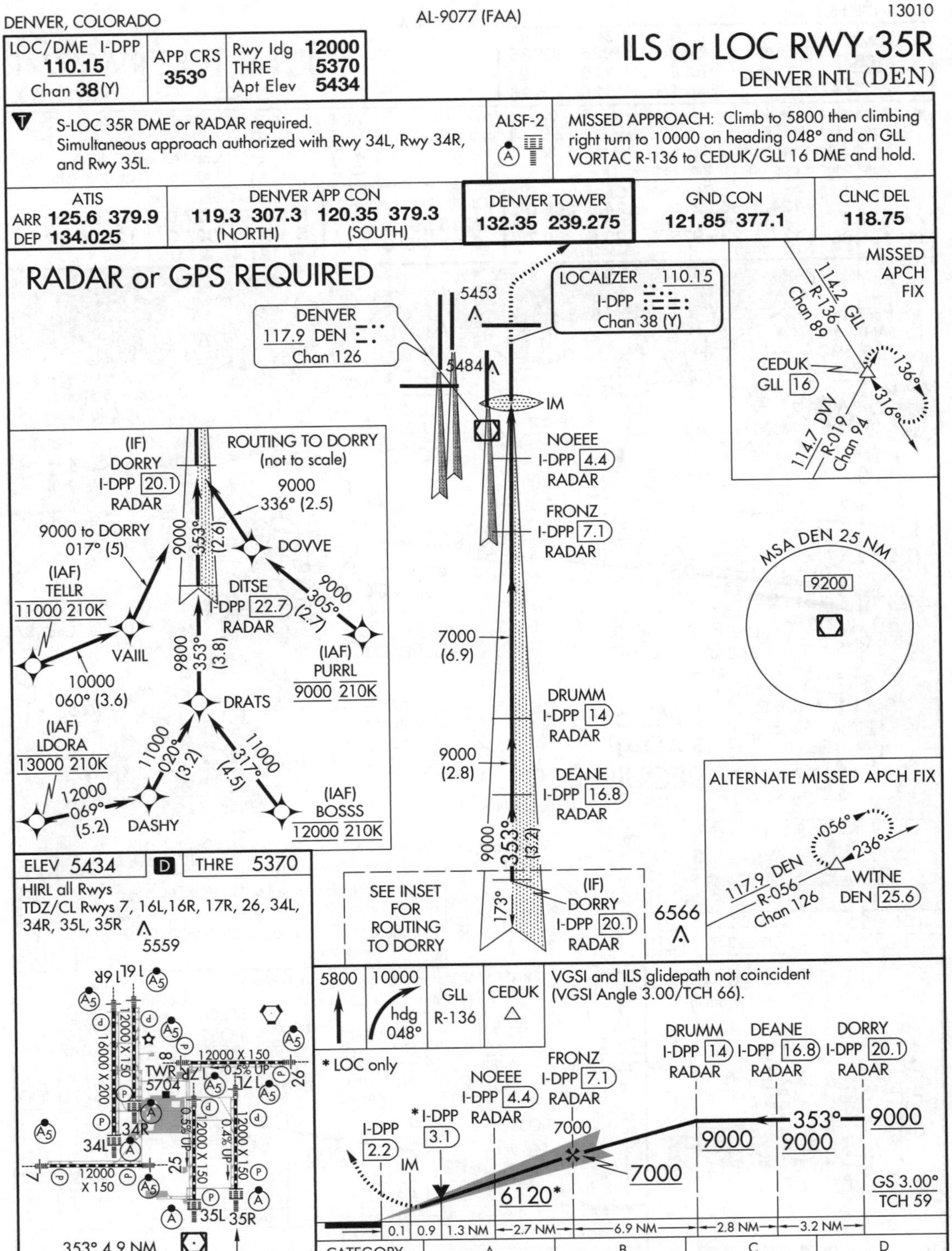

CATEGORY	A	B	C	D
S-ILS 35R	5570/18 200 (200-½)			
S-LOC 35R	5740/24 370 (400-½)		5740/35 370 (400-¾)	

FAF to MAP 4.9 NM					
Knots	60	90	120	150	180
Min:Sec	4:54	3:16	2:27	1:58	1:38

DENVER, COLORADO
Amdt 3 15NOV12
39°52'N-104°40'W
DENVER INTL (DEN)
ILS or LOC RWY 35R

Figure 27. ILS or LOC RWY 35R (DEN).

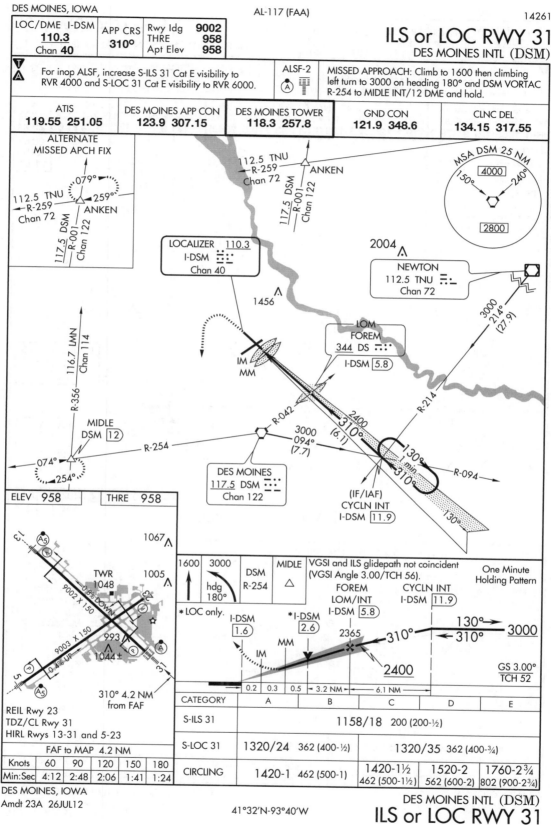

Figure 28. ILS or LOC RWY 31 (DSM).

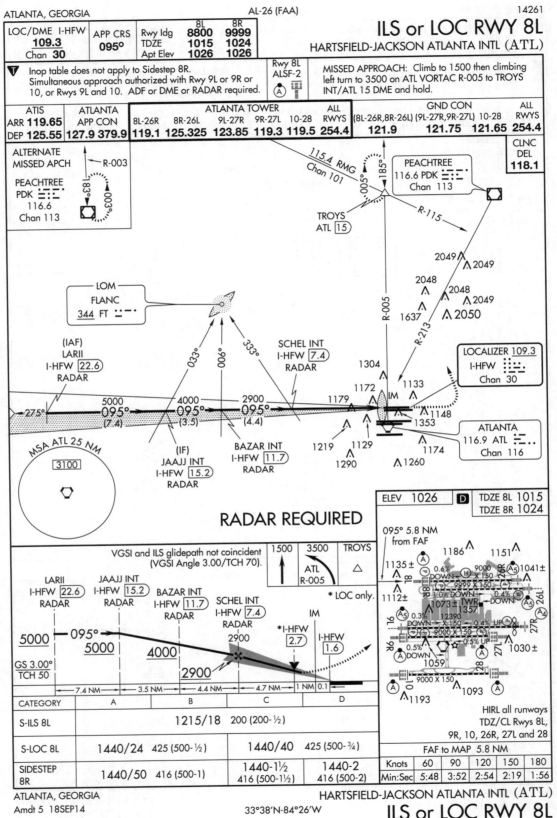

Figure 29. ILS or LOC RWY 8L (ATL).

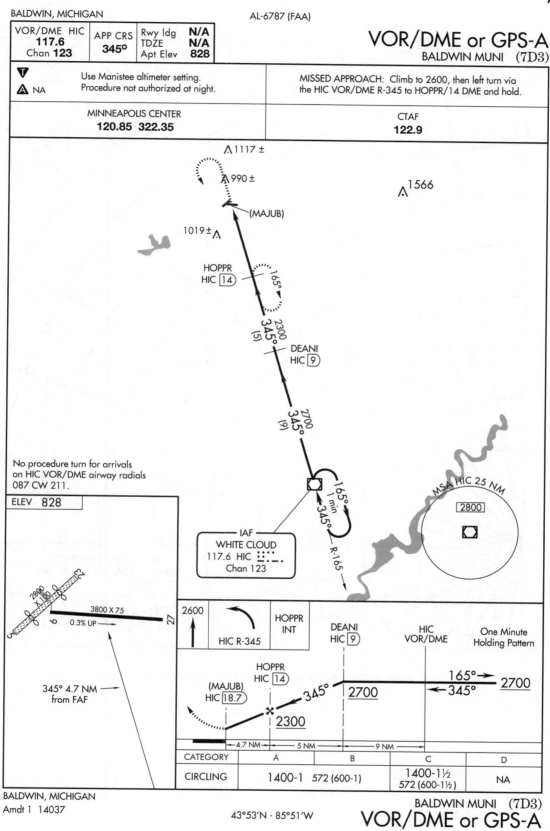

BALDWIN, MICHIGAN
AL-6787 (FAA)

VOR/DME HIC **117.6** Chan **123**	APP CRS **345°**	Rwy ldg **N/A** TDZE **N/A** Apt Elev **828**

VOR/DME or GPS-A
BALDWIN MUNI (7D3)

▼
⚠ NA Use Manistee altimeter setting. Procedure not authorized at night.

MISSED APPROACH: Climb to 2600, then left turn via the HIC VOR/DME R-345 to HOPPR/14 DME and hold.

MINNEAPOLIS CENTER **120.85 322.35**	CTAF **122.9**

△1117 ±
△ 990 ±
△1566
(MAJUB)
1019 ±△

HOPPR
HIC 14   165°

2300
345°
(5)

DEANI
HIC 9

2700
345°
(9)

No procedure turn for arrivals on HIC VOR/DME airway radials 087 CW 211.

165°
1 min
345°

IAF
WHITE CLOUD
117.6 HIC ⋮⋅⋯⋅
Chan 123

R-165

MSA HIC 25 NM
2800

ELEV 828

2900 X 100
3800 X 75
0.3% UP
9
27

345° 4.7 NM from FAF

2600	↑ HIC R-345	HOPPR INT	DEANI HIC 9	HIC VOR/DME	One Minute Holding Pattern

HOPPR HIC 14
(MAJUB) HIC 18.7
✗ 345°
2300
2700
2700
165°→
←345°

4.7 NM — 5 NM — 9 NM

CATEGORY	A	B	C	D
CIRCLING	1400-1 572 (600-1)		1400-1½ 572 (600-1½)	NA

BALDWIN, MICHIGAN
Amdt 1 14037

43°53'N - 85°51'W

BALDWIN MUNI (7D3)
VOR/DME or GPS-A

Figure 30. VOR/DME or GPS-A (7D3).

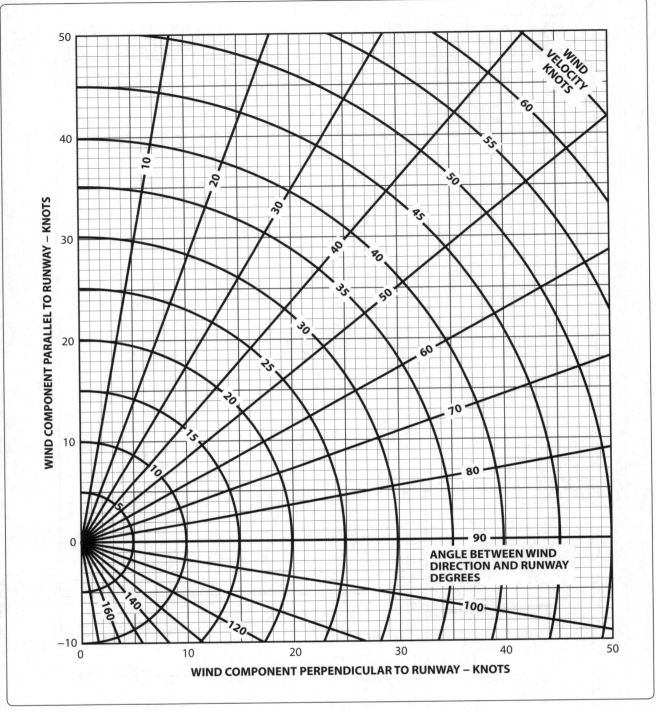

Figure 31. Wind Component Chart.

ASSOCIATED CONDITIONS:

POWER   TAKEOFF POWER
           SET BEFORE
           BRAKE RELEASE
FLAPS   20°
RUNWAY   PAVED, LEVEL, DRY SURFACE
TAKEOFF SPEED   IAS AS TABULATED

NOTE: GROUND ROLL IS APPROX 73% OF TOTAL TAKEOFF
        DISTANCE OVER A 50 FT OBSTACLE

EXAMPLE:

OAT	75 °F
PRESSURE ALTITUDE	4,000 FT
TAKEOFF WEIGHT	3,100 LB
HEADWIND	20 KNOTS

TOTAL TAKEOFF DISTANCE	
OVER A 50 FT OBSTACLE	1,350 FT
GROUND ROLL (73% OF 1,350)	986 FT
IAS TAKEOFF SPEED	
LIFT-OFF	74 MPH
AT 50 FT	74 MPH

WEIGHT (LB)	IAS TAKEOFF SPEED (ASSUMES ZERO INSTR ERROR)			
	LIFT-OFF		50 FEET	
	MPH	KNOTS	MPH	KNOTS
3,400	77	67	77	67
3,200	75	65	75	65
3,000	72	63	72	63
2,800	69	60	69	60
2,600	66	57	66	57
2,400	63	55	63	55

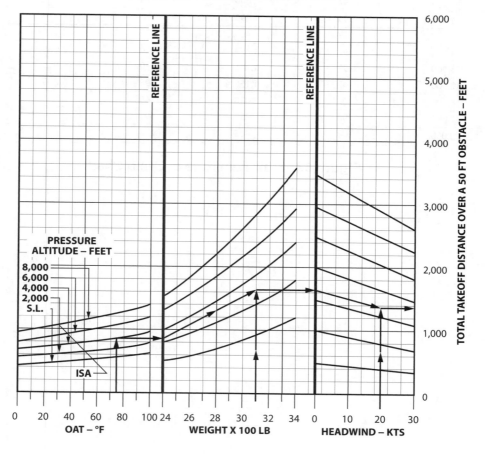

Figure 32. Obstacle Take-off Chart.

CONDITIONS:
FLAPS UP
GEAR UP
2,600 RPM
COWL FLAPS OPEN

PRESS ALT	MP	PPH
S.L. TO 17,000	35	162
18,000	34	156
20,000	32	144
22,000	30	132
24,000	28	120

WEIGHT (LB)	PRESS ALT (FT)	CLIMB SPEED (KIAS)	RATE OF CLIMB (FPM)			
			−20 °C	0 °C	20 °C	40 °C
4,000	S.L.	100	1,170	1,035	895	755
	4,000	100	1,080	940	800	655
	8,000	100	980	840	695	555
	12,000	100	870	730	590	---
	16,000	100	740	605	470	---
	20,000	99	485	355	---	---
	24,000	97	190	70	---	---
3,700	S.L.	99	1,310	1,165	1,020	875
	4,000	99	1,215	1,070	925	775
	8,000	99	1,115	965	815	670
	12,000	99	1,000	855	710	---
	16,000	99	865	730	590	---
	20,000	97	600	470	---	---
	24,000	95	295	170	---	---
3,400	S.L.	97	1,465	1,320	1,165	1,015
	4,000	97	1,370	1,220	1,065	910
	8,000	97	1,265	1,110	955	795
	12,000	97	1,150	995	845	---
	16,000	97	1,010	865	725	---
	20,000	96	730	595	---	---
	24,000	94	405	275	---	---

Figure 33. Maximum Rate of Climb Chart.

PRESSURE ALTITUDE 6,000 FEET

CONDITIONS:
3,800 POUNDS
RECOMMENDED LEAN MIXTURE
COWL FLAPS CLOSED

RPM	MP	20 °C BELOW STANDARD TEMPERATURE −17 °C			STANDARD TEMPERATURE 3 °C			20 °C ABOVE STANDARD TEMPERATURE 23 °C		
		% BHP	KTAS	PPH	% BHP	KTAS	PPH	% BHP	KTAS	PPH
2,550	24	---	---	---	78	173	97	75	174	94
	23	76	167	96	74	169	92	71	171	89
	22	72	164	90	69	166	87	67	167	84
	21	68	160	85	65	162	82	63	163	80
2,500	24	78	169	98	75	171	95	73	172	91
	23	74	166	93	71	167	90	69	169	87
	22	70	162	88	67	164	85	65	165	82
	21	66	158	83	63	160	80	61	160	77
2,400	24	73	165	91	70	166	88	68	167	85
	23	69	161	87	67	163	84	64	164	81
	22	65	158	82	63	159	79	61	160	77
	21	61	154	77	59	155	75	57	155	73
2,300	24	68	161	86	66	162	83	64	163	80
	23	65	158	82	62	159	79	60	159	76
	22	61	154	77	59	155	75	57	155	72
	21	57	150	73	55	150	71	53	150	68
2,200	24	63	156	80	61	157	77	59	158	75
	23	60	152	76	58	153	73	56	154	71
	22	57	149	72	54	149	70	53	149	67
	21	53	144	68	51	144	66	49	143	64
	20	50	139	64	48	138	62	46	137	60
	19	46	133	60	44	132	58	43	131	57

Figure 34. Cruise Performance Chart.

ASSOCIATED CONDITIONS:

POWER   AS REQUIRED TO MAINTAIN 800 FT/MIN
           DESCENT ON APPROACH
FLAPS   DOWN
RUNWAY   PAVED, LEVEL, DRY SURFACE
APPROACH SPEED   IAS AS TABULATED

NOTE: GROUND ROLL IS APPROX 53% OF TOTAL LANDING
          DISTANCE OVER A 50 FT OBSTACLE.

EXAMPLE:

OAT	75 °F
PRESSURE ALTITUDE	4,000 FT
LANDING WEIGHT	3,200 LB
HEADWIND	10 KNOTS

TOTAL LANDING DISTANCE	
OVER A 50 FT OBSTACLE	1,475 FT
GROUND ROLL (53% OF 1,475)	782 FT
IAS TAKEOFF SPEED	87 MPH IAS

WEIGHT (LB)	IAS APPROACH SPEED (ASSUMES ZERO INSTR ERROR)	
	MPH	KNOTS
3,400	90	78
3,200	87	76
3,000	84	73
2,800	81	70
2,600	78	68
2,400	75	65

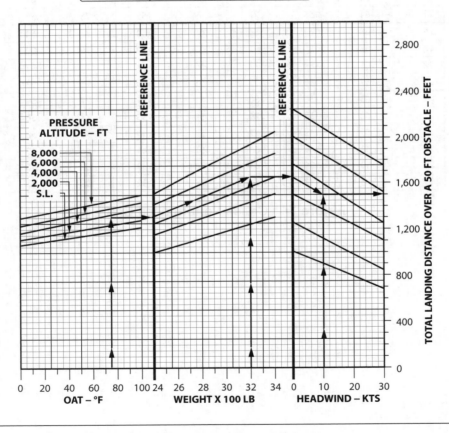

Figure 35. Normal Landing Chart.

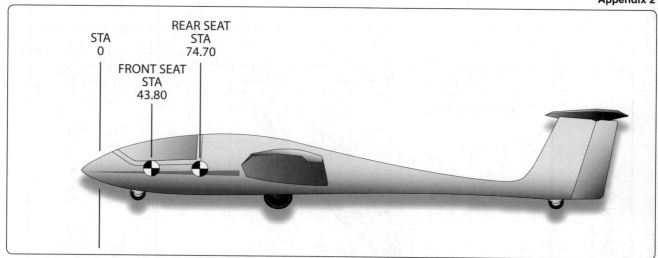

Figure 36. Stations Diagram.

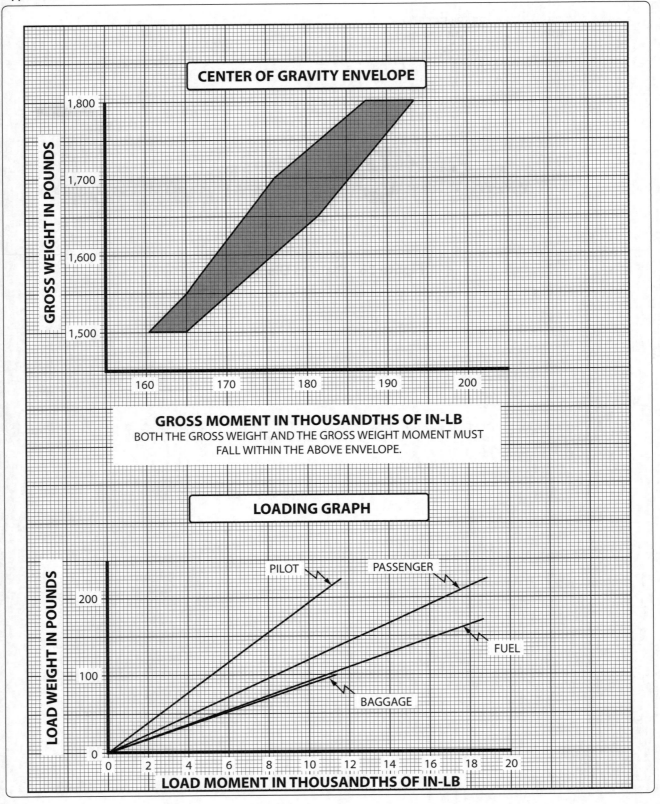

Figure 37. Center of Gravity Envelope and Loading Graph.

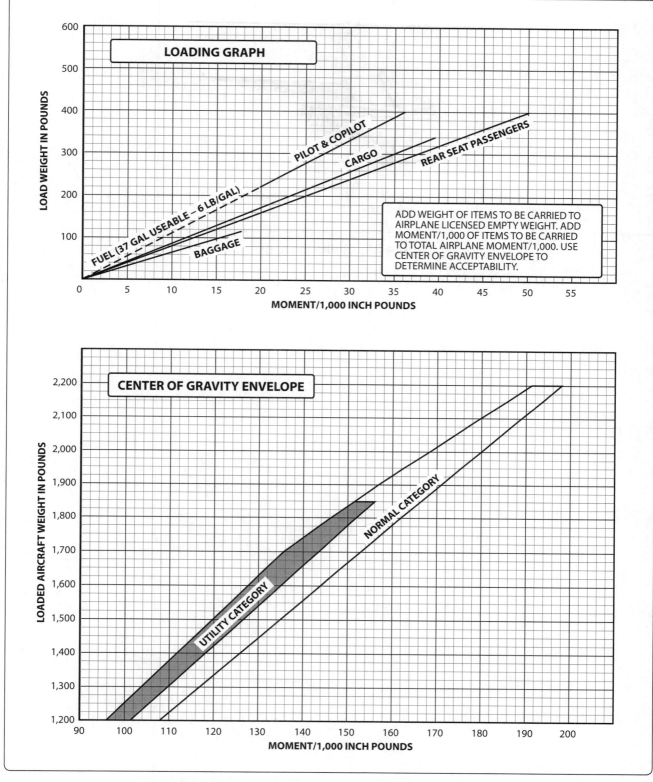

Figure 38. Loading Graph and Center of Gravity Envelope.

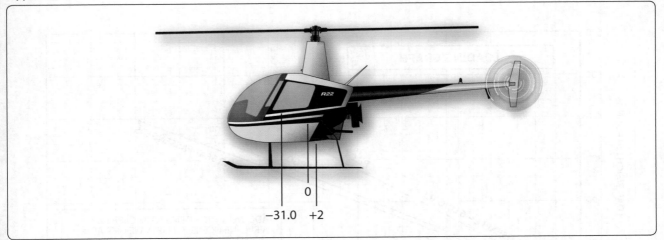

Figure 39. Stations Diagram.

THE FOLLOWING CG LOCATIONS MAY BE USED WHEN DETERMINING THE HELICOPTER CG POSITION.

ITEM	LONG CG	LAT CG
PILOT & BAGGAGE UNDER "R" SEAT	79.0	+10.7
PASSENGER & BAGGAGE UNDER "L" SEAT	79.0	−9.3
MAIN FUEL	108.6	−11.0
AUX FUEL (OPTIONAL)	103.8	+11.2

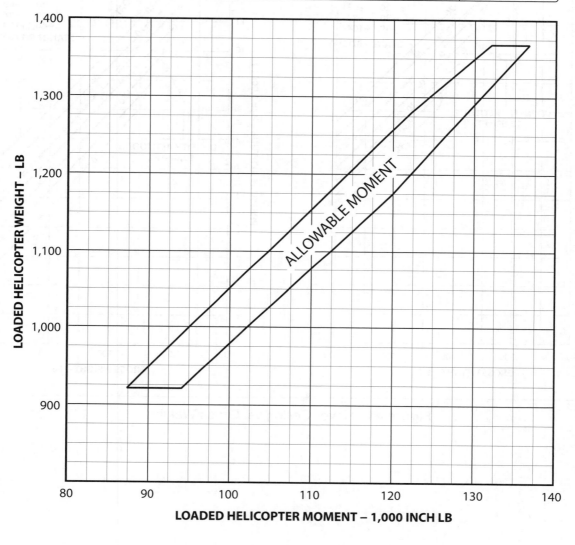

Figure 40. Weight and Balance Chart.

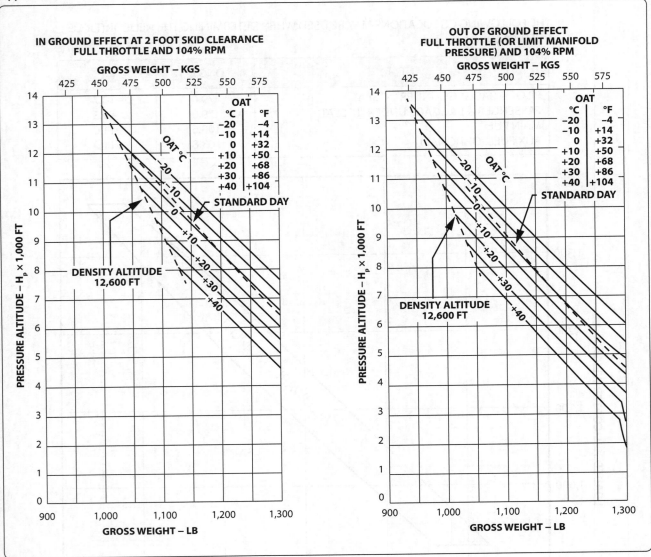

Figure 41. Hover Ceiling vs. Gross Weight.

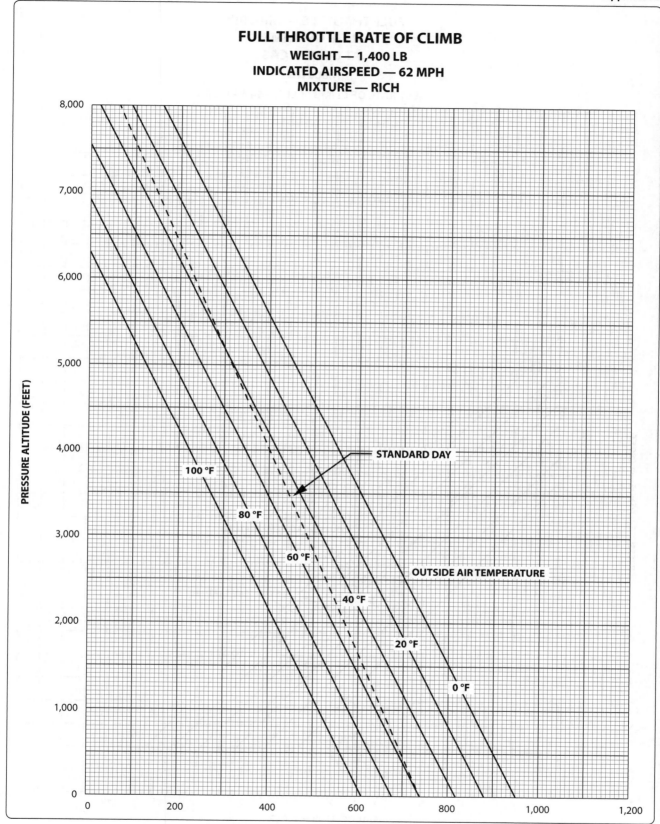

Figure 42. Rate of Climb (FT/MIN).

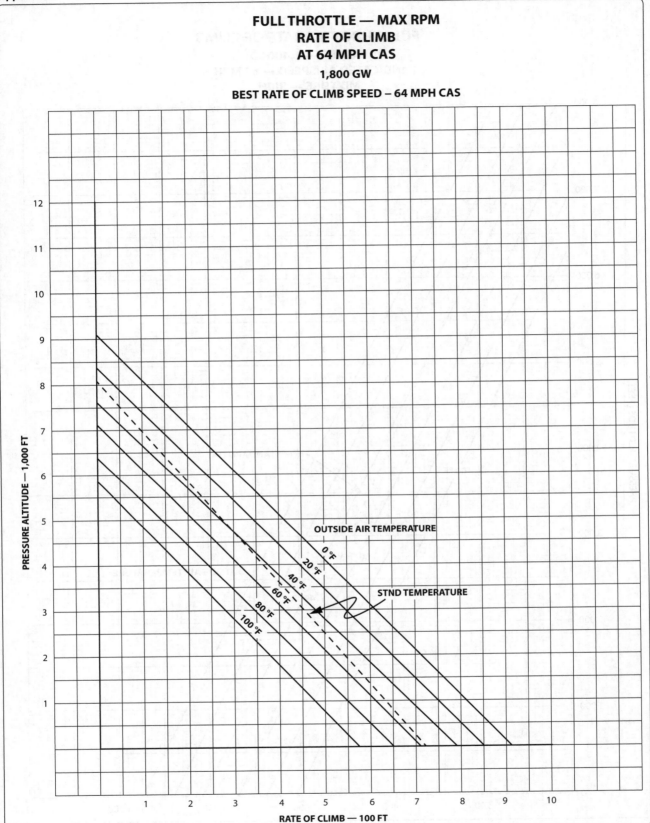

Figure 43. Best Rate of Climb Speed.

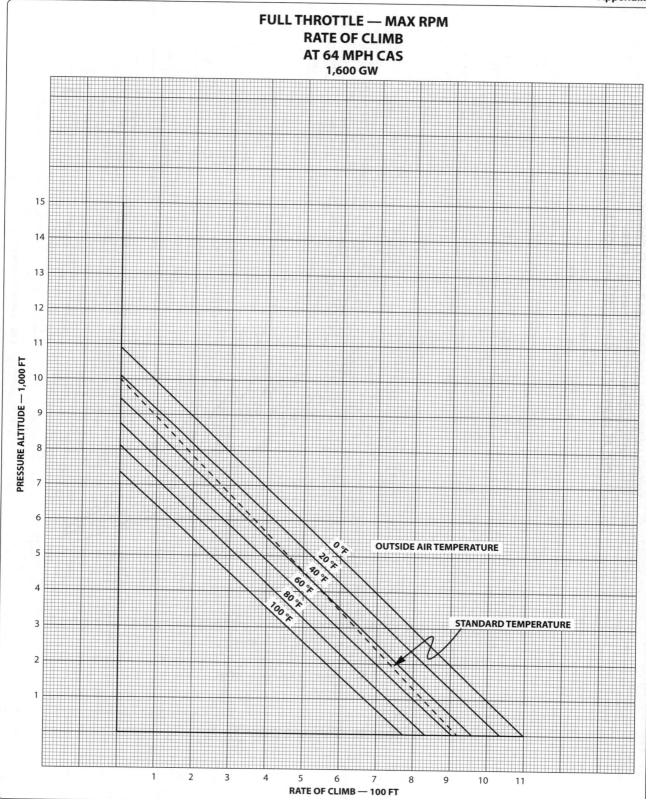

Figure 44. Rate of Climb.

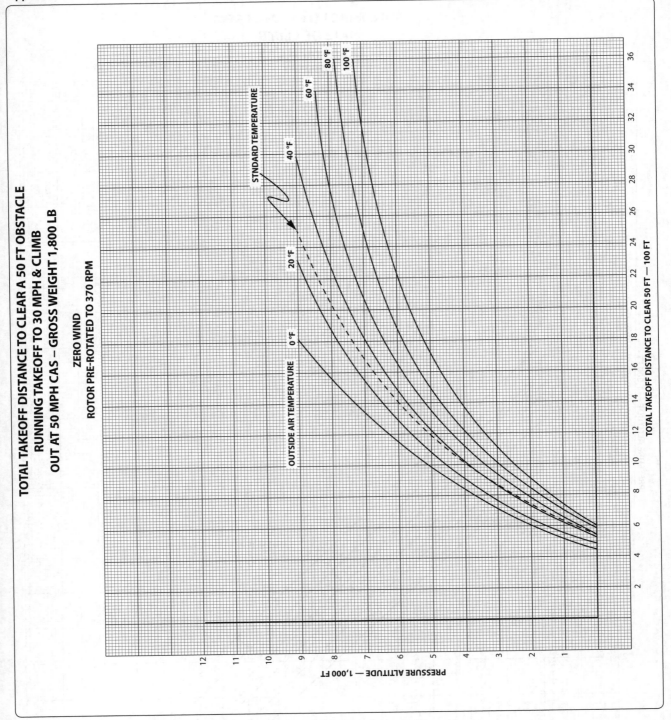

Figure 45. Running Takeoff.

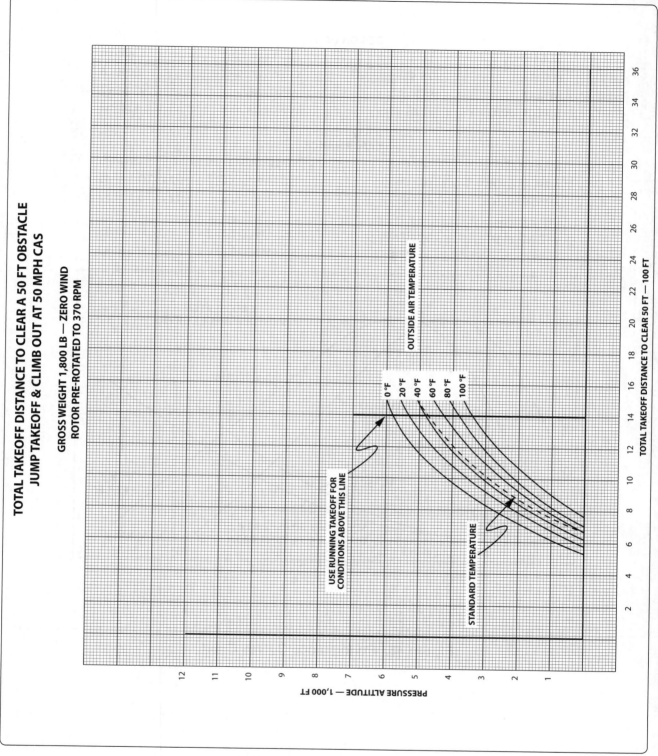

Figure 46. Jump Takeoff.

DESIGN DATA

WING SPAN	51'	EMPTY WEIGHT	600 LB
LENGTH	25' 9"	GROSS WEIGHT	1,040 LB
HEIGHT	9' 3-½"	WING AREA	219.5 SQ FT
ASPECT RATIO	11.85	WING LOADING	4.74 PSF

PERFORMANCE

MAX SPEED	98 MPH	STALL (DUAL)	35 MPH
AIRPLANE TOW	98 MPH	L/D MPH (SOLO)	22.25 TO 1 AT 45
AUTO WINCH	69 MPH	L/D MPH (DUAL)	22.25 TO 1 AT 52
DRIVE BRAKE			
EXTEND. MAX	98 MPH	SINK SPEED (SOLO)	2.6 FPS AT 38
STALL (SOLO)	31 MPH	SINK SPEED (DUAL)	3.1 FPS AT 42

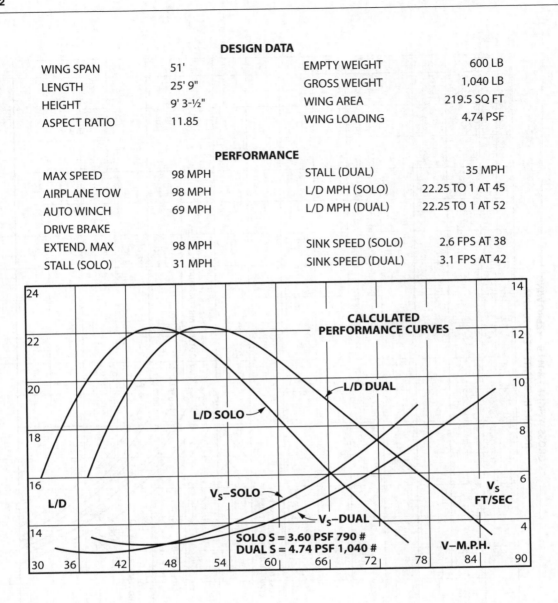

Figure 48. Performance Curves Chart.

PERFORMANCE CURVES GROSS WEIGHT = 575 LB

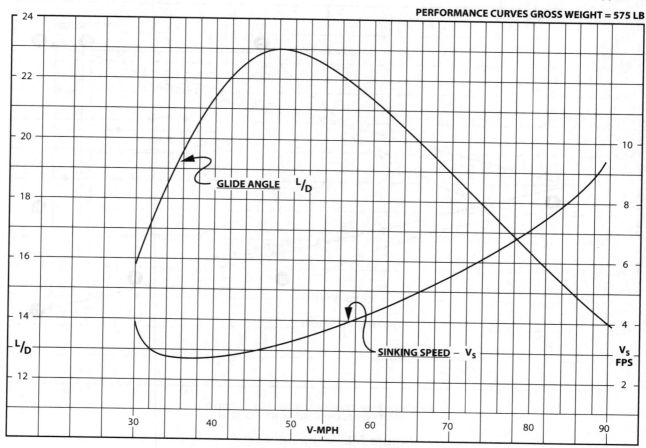

Figure 49. Performance Curves Chart.

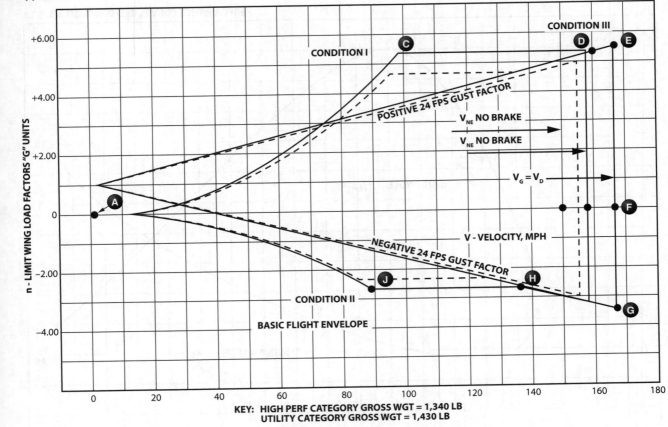

Figure 50. Flight Envelope.

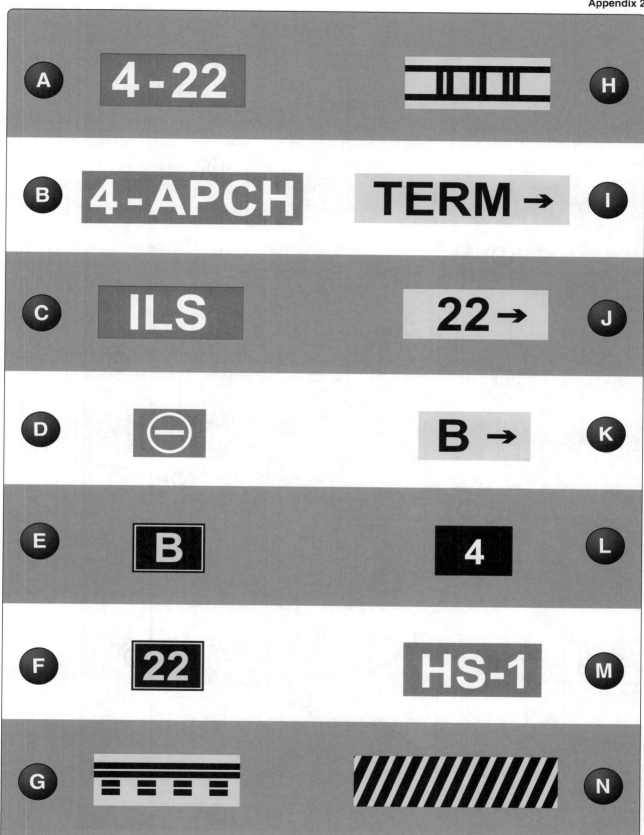

Figure 51. Airport Signs.

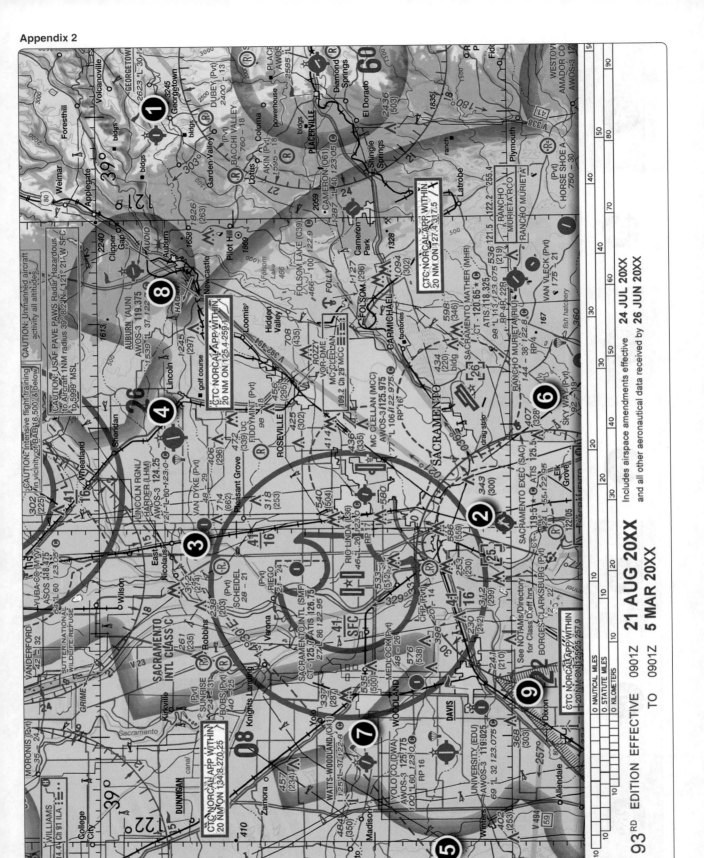

Figure 52. Sectional Chart Excerpt.

Note: Chart is not to scale and should not be used for navigation. Chart is for testing purposes only.

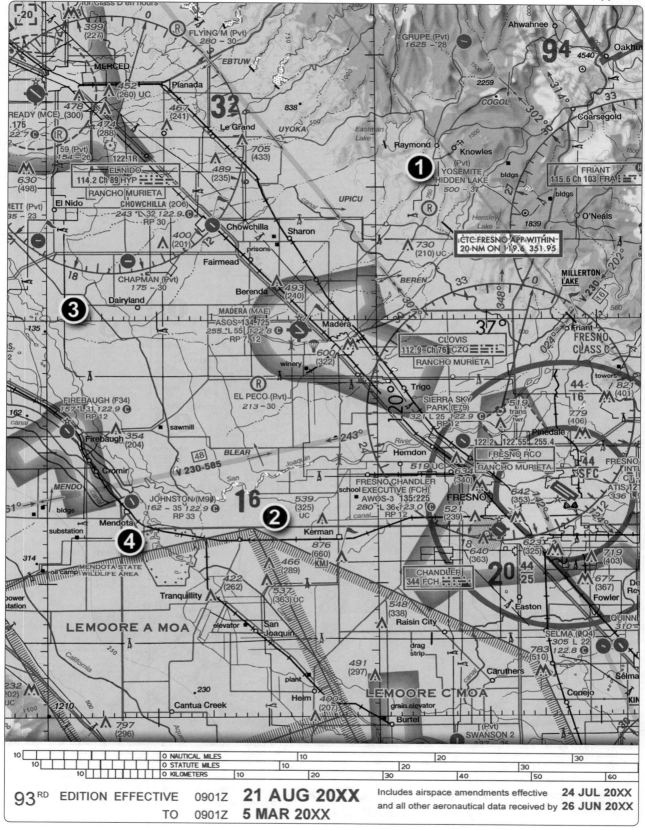

Figure 53. Sectional Chart Excerpt.

Note: Chart is not to scale and should not be used for navigation. Chart is for testing purposes only.

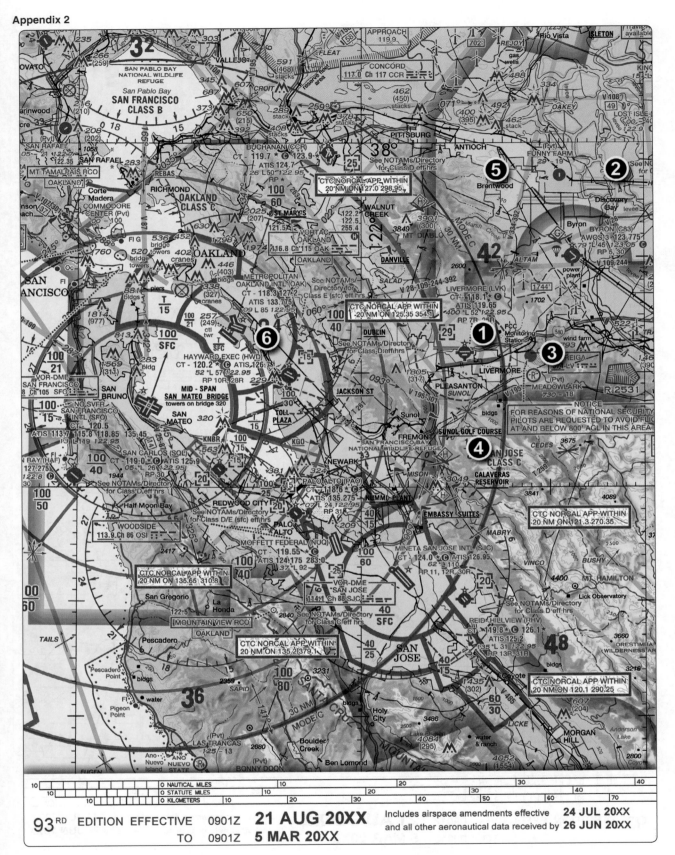

Figure 54. Sectional Chart Excerpt.

Note: Chart is not to scale and should not be used for navigation. Chart is for testing purposes only.

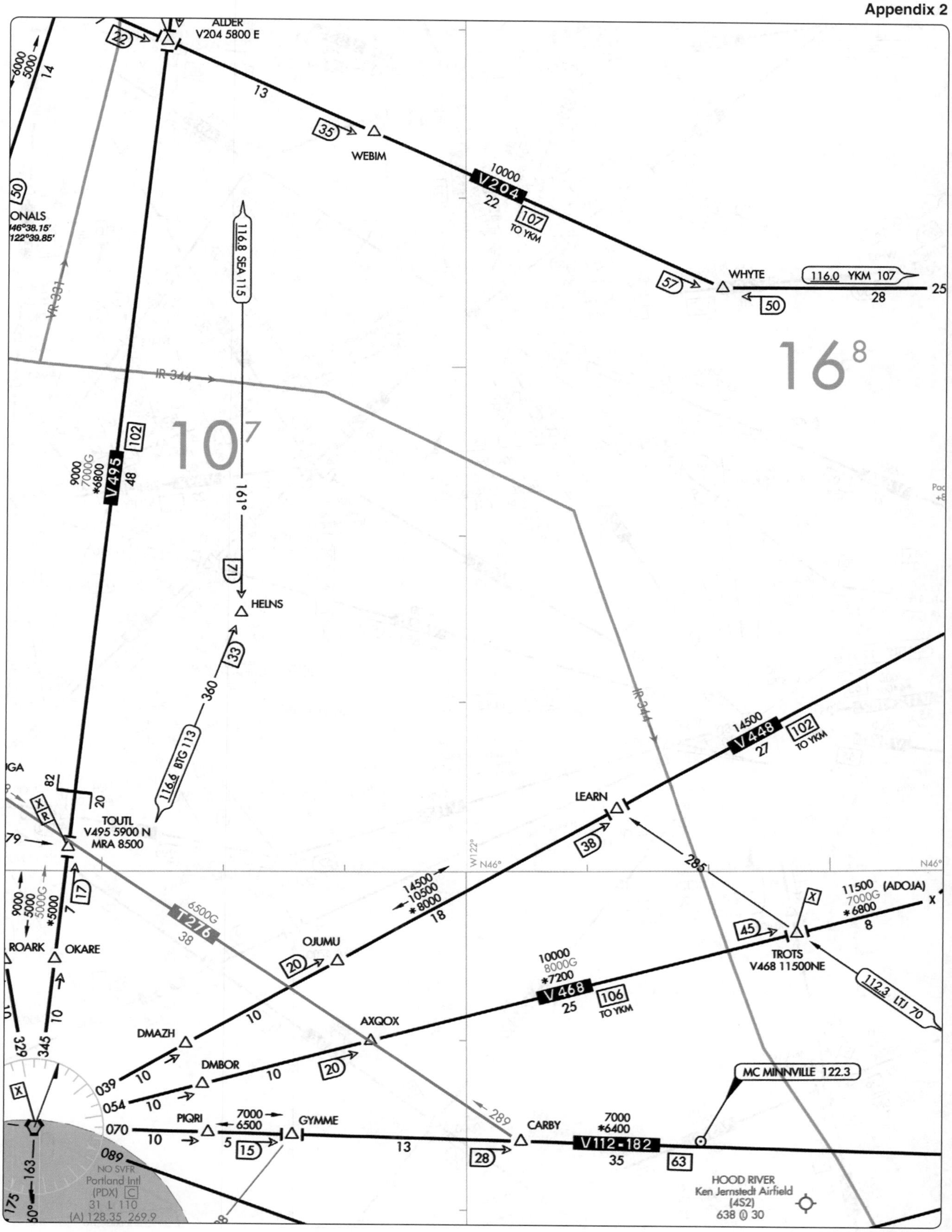

Figure 55. En Route Low Altitude Segment.

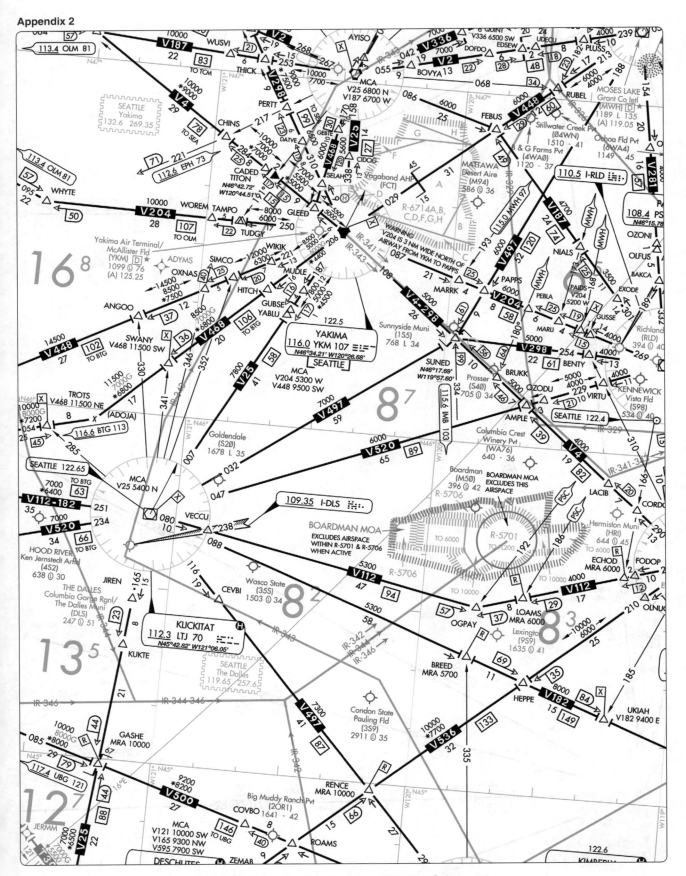

Figure 55A. En Route Low Altitude Segment.

2-44

Figure 56. Two signs.

Figure 57. Sign.

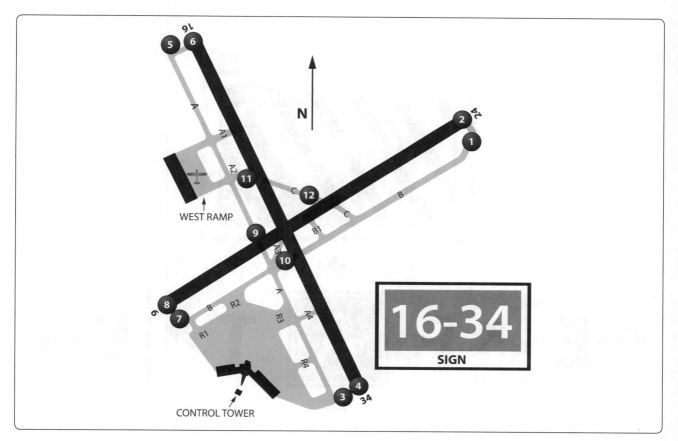

Figure 58. Airport Diagram and Sign.

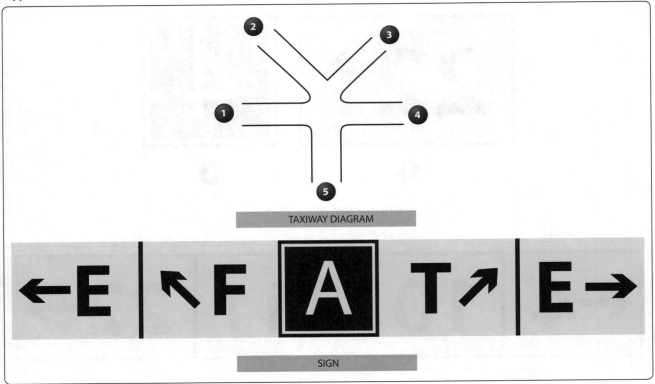

Figure 59. Taxiway Diagram and Sign.

Figure 60. Two Signs.

Figure 61. Sign.

Figure 62. Sign.

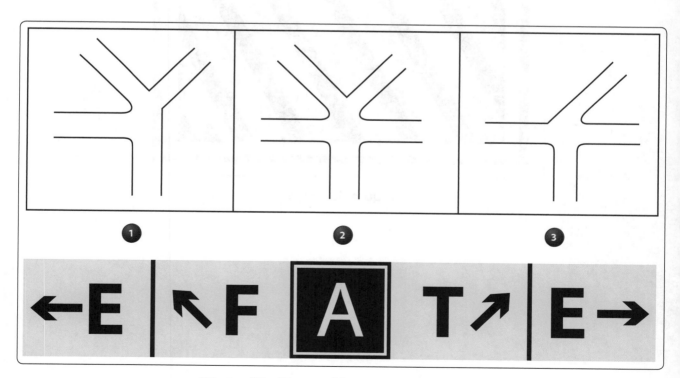

Figure 63. Sign and Intersection Diagram.

Figure 64. Sign.

Figure 65. Sign.

200

OKLAHOMA

WILEY POST (PWA)(KPWA) 7 NW UTC–6(–5DT) N35°32.05′ W97°38.82′

1300 B TPA—See Remarks NOTAM FILE PWA

RWY 17L–35R: H7199X150 (CONC) S–35, D–50, 2D–90 HIRL

  RWY 17L: MALSR. PAPI(P4L)—GA 3.0° TCH 54′. Rgt tfc.

  RWY 35R: MALSR. PAPI(P4L)—GA 3.0° TCH 54′. Thld dsplcd 355′. Trees.

RWY 17R–35L: H5002X75 (ASPH–CONC) S–26, D–45 MIRL

  RWY 17R: REIL. PAPI(P4L)—GA 3.0° TCH 43′. Tree. Rgt tfc.

  RWY 35L: REIL. PAPI(P4L)—GA 3.0° TCH 42′.

RWY 13–31: H4214X100 (CONC) S–35, D–50, 2D–90 MIRL

  0.6% up SE

  RWY 13: Rgt tfc.

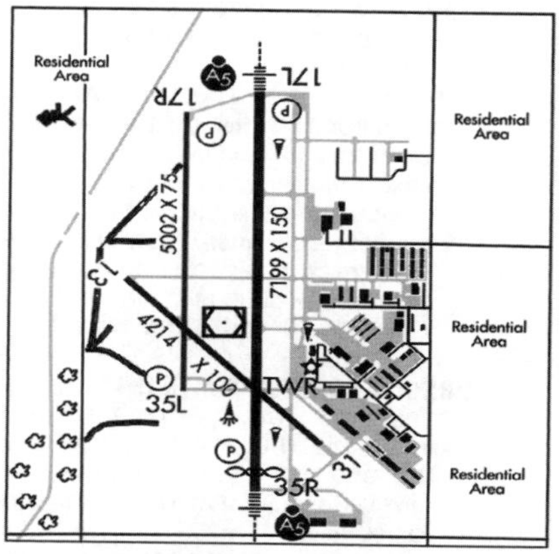

RUNWAY DECLARED DISTANCE INFORMATION

RWY 13:	TORA–4214	TODA–4214	ASDA–4214	LDA–4214
RWY 17L:	TORA–7199	TODA–7199	ASDA–6844	LDA–6844
RWY 17R:	TORA–5002	TODA–5002	ASDA–5002	LDA–5002
RWY 31:	TORA–4214	TODA–4214	ASDA–4214	LDA–4214
RWY 35L:	TORA–5001	TODA–5001	ASDA–5001	LDA–5001
RWY 35R:	TORA–7198	TODA–7198	ASDA–7198	LDA–6844

SERVICE: S4 **FUEL** 100LL, JET A **OX** 1, 2, 3, 4 **LGT** Dusk–Dawn. When twr clsd ACTIVATE HIRL Rwy 17L–35R and MALSR Rwy 17L and Rwy 35R—CTAF.

AIRPORT REMARKS: Attended continuously. 100LL fuel avbl 24 hrs self serve with credit card. Surface conditions reported Mon–Fri 1400–2300Z‡. Rwy 13–31 CLOSED 0400–1300Z‡. Rwy 13–31 CLOSED to tkof and Rwy 31 CLOSED to acft over 12,500 lbs gross weight. Flocks of birds on and invof arpt all quadrants. Noise abatement procedure: Acft in excess of 12,500 pounds departing Rwy 17L–35R climb at a maximum rate consistent with safety to an altitude of 1500′ AGL then reduce power setting and climb rate to 3000′ AGL or 2 NM from arpt depending on air traffic control and safety conditions. TPA for Rwy 17R/35L 1900(600) 2300(1000) all other rwys. Rwy 13–31 unlighted 0400–1300Z‡. Touch & go or stop & go ldgs not authorized Rwy 13–31.

AIRPORT MANAGER: 405-316-4061

WEATHER DATA SOURCES: ASOS (405) 798–2013

COMMUNICATIONS: CTAF 126.9 **ATIS** 128.725 **UNICOM** 122.95

  RCO 122.65 (MC ALESTER RADIO)

Ⓡ **OKE CITY APP/DEP CON** 124.6 (171°–360°) 120.45 (081°–170°) 124.2 (001°–080°)

  TOWER 126.9 (1300–0400Z‡) **GND CON** 121.7

AIRSPACE: CLASS D svc 1300–0400Z‡ other times CLASS E.

RADIO AIDS TO NAVIGATION: NOTAM FILE PWA.

  (T) VORW/DME 113.4 PWA Chan 81 N35°31.98′ W97°38.83′ at fld. 1271/8E.

  ILS 110.15 I–PWA Rwy 17L. Unmonitored when ATCT clsd. DME also serves Rwy 35R.

  ILS/DME 110.15 I–TFM Chan 38(Y) Rwy 35R. Class IT. DME also serves Rwy 17L.

Figure 66. Chart Supplement.

LUBBOCK

LUBBOCK EXECUTIVE AIRPARK (F82)   5 S   UTC–6(–5DT)   N33°29.14´ W101°48.76´   DALLAS–FT WORTH L–6H
  3200   B   TPA—4200(1000)   NOTAM FILE FTW
  RWY 17–35: H3500X70 (ASPH)   S–13   HIRL
  RWY 07–25: 1500X110 (TURF)
    RWY 07: P–line.
  SERVICE: S4   **FUEL** 100LL, JET A
  AIRPORT REMARKS: Attended 1400–0000Z‡. After hrs 806–789–6437, 806–589–8143. Fuel avbl 24 hrs with major credit
    card. Rwy 17 road located at thld. Farm equipment ops AER 17, Rwy 25 and Rwy 35.
  AIRPORT MANAGER: 806–789–6437
  COMMUNICATIONS: CTAF/UNICOM 122.8
  RADIO AIDS TO NAVIGATION: NOTAM FILE LBB.
    (L) VORTACW 109.2   LBB   Chan 29   N33°42.30´ W101°54.84´   148° 14.1 NM to fld. 3310/11E.   **HIWAS.**
    VOR portion unusable:
      140°–190° byd 20 NM blo 5,100´

- -

LUBBOCK PRESTON SMITH INTL (LBB)(KLBB)   4 N   UTC–6(–5DT)   N33°39.82´ W101°49.23´   DALLAS–FT WORTH H–6G, L–6H
  3282   B   LRA   Class I, ARFF Index C   NOTAM FILE LBB   IAP, AD
  RWY 17R–35L: H11500X150 (CONC–GRVD)   S–100, D–170, 2S–175,
    2D–350 PCN 65 R/B/W/T   HIRL
    RWY 17R: MALSR. PAPI(P4R)—GA 3.0° TCH 69´. RVR–T Rgt tfc.
    0.4% down.
    RWY 35L: ODALS. VASI(V4L)—GA 3.0° TCH 54´. RVR–R 0.3% up.
  RWY 08–26: H8003X150 (CONC–GRVD)   S–100, D–170, 2S–175,
    2D–350 PCN 71 R/B/W/T   HIRL
    RWY 08: REIL. PAPI(P4L)—GA 3.0° TCH 50´. RVR–R Rgt tfc.
    RWY 26: MALSR. PAPI(P4L)—GA 3.0° TCH 50´. RVR–T
  RWY 17L–35R: H2891X74 (ASPH)   S–12.5
    RWY 35R: Road. Rgt tfc. 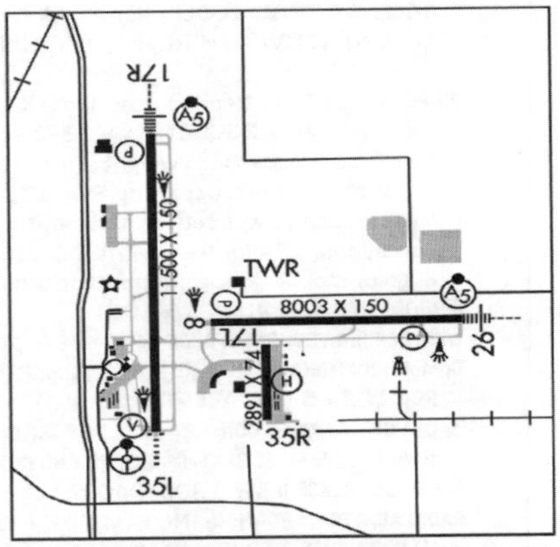
  RUNWAY DECLARED DISTANCE INFORMATION
    RWY 08: TORA–8003   TODA–8003   ASDA–8003   LDA–8003
    RWY 17L: TORA–2891   TODA–2891   ASDA–2891   LDA–2891
    RWY 17R: TORA–11500 TODA–11500 ASDA–11500 LDA–11500
    RWY 26: TORA–8003   TODA–8003   ASDA–8003   LDA–8003
    RWY 35L: TORA–11500 TODA–11500 ASDA–11500 LDA–11500
    RWY 35R: TORA–2891   TODA–2891   ASDA–2891   LDA–2891
  SERVICE: S4   **FUEL** 100LL, JET A, A1+   **OX** 1, 2, 3, 4

  AIRPORT REMARKS: Attended continuously. Numerous birds on and invof
    arpt. PAEW adjacent Rwy 08–26 and Rwy 17R–35L. Passenger terminal ramp access rstd to air carriers and others with
    prior permission call 806–775–2044. Rwy 17L–35R rstd to general aviation acft 12,500 lbs or less. Rwy 17L–35R, Twy
    B, Twy D, and Twy E not avbl for air carrier acft with over 9 psgr seats. Twy B, Twy D, and Twy E rstd to acft weighing
    less than 50,000 lbs. Twy L between Twy F and Twy J clsd to more than 120,001 lbs. East ramp delineated taxilane and
    apron area rstd to 120,000 lbs dual tandem acft, 89,000 lbs dual single wheel acft and 60,000 lbs single wheel acft.
    All other east ramp pavements rstd to acft less than 12,500 lbs single wheel acft. Flight Notification Service (ADCUS)
    available.
  AIRPORT MANAGER: 806–775–3126
  WEATHER DATA SOURCES: ASOS 125.3 (806) 766–6432. **HIWAS** 109.2 LBB. WSP.
  COMMUNICATIONS: ATIS 125.3 **UNICOM** 122.95
    RCO 122.55 (FORT WORTH RADIO)
  Ⓡ **APP/DEP CON** 119.2 119.9
    TOWER 120.5 **GND CON** 121.9 **CLNC DEL** 125.8
  AIRSPACE: CLASS C svc ctc **APP CON**
  RADIO AIDS TO NAVIGATION: NOTAM FILE LBB.
    (L) VORTACW 109.2   LBB   Chan 29   N33°42.30´ W101°54.84´   107° 5.3 NM to fld. 3310/11E.   **HIWAS.**
    VOR portion unusable:
      140°–190° byd 20 NM blo 5,100´
    LUBBI NDB (LOMW) 272   LD   N33°39.76´ W101°43.39´   265° 4.9 NM to fld. 3198/6E.
    POLLO NDB (LOM) 219   LB   N33°44.26´ W101°49.76´ 168° 4.5 NM to fld.
    ILS/DME 111.7   I–LBB   Chan 54   Rwy 17R. Class IA. LOM POLLO NDB.
    ILS 111.9   I–LDT   Rwy 26. Class IA. LOM LUBBI NDB.

Figure 67. Chart Supplement.

DALLAS

ADDISON (ADS)(KADS)   9 N   UTC–6(–5DT)   N32°58.11´ W96°50.19´   **DALLAS–FT WORTH**
645   B   TPA—See Remarks   LRA   NOTAM FILE ADS   **COPTER**
RWY 15–33: H7203X100 (ASPH–GRVD)   S–60, D–120   HIRL   H–6H, L–17C, A
    RWY 15: MALSR. PAPI(P4R)—GA 3.0° TCH 60´. Thld dsplcd 979´.   IAP, AD
    Tree.
    RWY 33: REIL. PAPI(P4L)—GA 3.0° TCH 60´. Thld dsplcd 772´. Bldg.
RUNWAY DECLARED DISTANCE INFORMATION
    RWY 15: TORA–7203   TODA–7203   ASDA–7203   LDA–6224
    RWY 33: TORA–7203   TODA–7203   ASDA–7203   LDA–6431
ARRESTING GEAR/SYSTEM
    RWY 15: EMAS
SERVICE: S4   **FUEL** 100LL, JET A   **OX** 2, 3   **LGT** ACTIVATE HIRL Rwy
    15–33 and MALSR Rwy 15—CTAF.
AIRPORT REMARKS: Attended continuously. Birds on and invof arpt. No
    touch and go ldgs without arpt mgr apvl. Numerous 200´ bldgs within
    1 mile east, and south of arpt, transmission twrs and water tanks west
    of arpt. Noise sensitive areas surround arpt. Pilots req to use NBAA std
    noise procedures. TPA—1601 (956) for light acft, 2001 (1356) for
    large acft. Be alert, rwy holding position markings lctd at the west
    edge of Twy A. Flight Notification Service (ADCUS) available.
AIRPORT MANAGER: 972-392-4850
WEATHER DATA SOURCES: AWOS–3 (972) 386–4855 LAWRS.
COMMUNICATIONS: CTAF 126.0   **ATIS** 133.4 972–628–2439
UNICOM 122.95
Ⓡ**REGIONAL APP/DEP CON** 124.3
    TOWER 126.0 (1200–0400Z‡)   **GND CON** 121.6   **CLNC DEL** 119.55
AIRSPACE: CLASS D svc 1200–0400Z‡, other times CLASS G.
RADIO AIDS TO NAVIGATION: NOTAM FILE FTW.
    MAVERICK (H) VORW/DME 113.1   TTT   Chan 78   N32°52.15´ W97°02.43´   054° 11.9 NM to fld. 540/6E.
        All acft arriving DFW are requested to turn DME off until departure due to traffic overload of Maverick DME
    DME unusable:
        180°–190°
    ILS/DME 110.1   I–ADS   Chan 38   Rwy 15.   Class IT.   Unmonitored when ATCT closed. DME also serves Rwy 33.
    ILS/DME 110.1   I–TBQ   Chan 38   Rwy 33.   Class IB.   Localizer unmonitored when ATCT closed. DME also serves
    Rwy 15.

- -

AIR PARK–DALLAS (F69)   16 NE   UTC–6(–5DT)   N33°01.41´ W96°50.22´   **DALLAS–FT WORTH**
695   TPA—1890(1195)   NOTAM FILE FTW   **COPTER**
RWY 16–34: H3080X30 (ASPH)   LIRL(NSTD)   L–17C, A
    RWY 16: Thld dsplcd 300´. Pole.
    RWY 34: Tree. Rgt tfc.
SERVICE: S4   **FUEL** 100LL   **LGT** ACTIVATE LIRL Rwy 16–34—CTAF. Rwy 16–34 NSTD LIRL; 2780´ of rwy lgtd. Thld and
    dsplcd thld not lighted.
AIRPORT REMARKS: Uattended. For fuel call 972–248–4265 prior to arr. Rwy 16–34 pavement cracking, loose stones on rwy.
    Rwy 34 NSTD cntrln marking incorrect size and spacing.   Rwy numbers 25´ tall, markings faded.   Rwy number 34 not
    located at rwy end.
AIRPORT MANAGER: 972–248–4265
COMMUNICATIONS: CTAF 122.9
RADIO AIDS TO NAVIGATION: NOTAM FILE FTW.
    MAVERICK (H) VORW/DME 113.1   TTT   Chan 78   N32°52.15´ W97°02.43´   042° 13.8 NM to fld. 540/6E.
        All acft arriving DFW are requested to turn DME off until departure due to traffic overload of Maverick DME
    DME unusable:
        180°–190°
COMM/NAV/WEATHER REMARKS: For Clnc Del ctc Regional Apch at 972–615–2799.

- -

Figure 68. Chart Supplement.

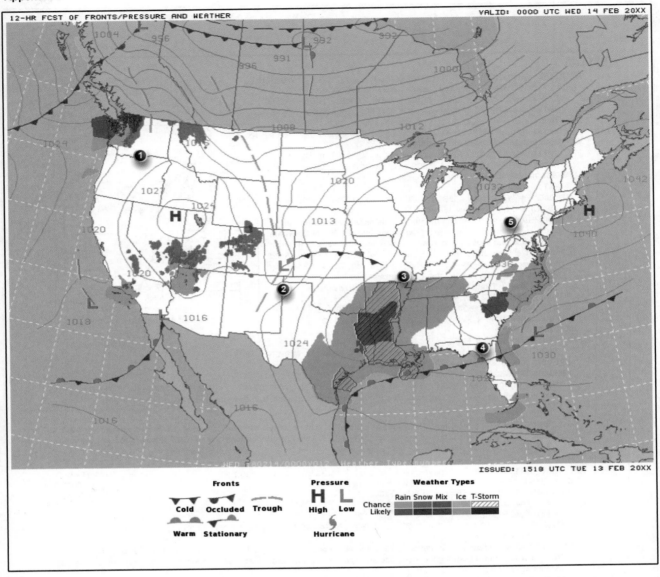

Figure 69. Weather Prediction Center (WPC) Surface Prog Chart.